# Streamline ENGLISH

## BERNARD HARTLEY & PETER VINEY

## DESTINATIONS

## WORKBOOK B
## UNITS 41–80

Oxford University Press

Oxford University Press
Walton Street, Oxford OX2 6DP

London New York
Toronto Delhi Bombay Calcutta
Madras Karachi Kuala Lumpur
Singapore Hong Kong Tokyo
Nairobi Dar Es Salaam
Cape Town Melbourne Auckland

and associated companies in
Beirut Berlin Ibadan Mexico City
Nicosia

OXFORD is a trade mark of Oxford
University Press

ISBN 0 19 432237 8 (workbook A)
ISBN 0 19 432238 6 (workbook B)
ISBN 0 19 432241 6 (student's edition)
ISBN 0 19 432242 4 (teacher's edition)
ISBN 0 19 432243 2 (set of 3 cassettes)

*Illustrations by:*
Edward McLachlan
*The publishers would like to thank the*
*following for permission to reproduce*
*copyright material:*
The Countryside Commission for the
leaflet, 'Follow the Country Code';
the Automobile Association for the
extract from 'AA Town Plans' (2nd
edition); the Daily Mail, London for
the article, 'Piranha bites a baby's
hand'; Agence France Press for the
article, 'Woman of 93 hit cabbie with her
walking stick'; Random House, Inc. for
the extract from Truman Capote: 'Music
for Chameleons'; British Airways for the
leaflet, 'Bermuda'.
*The publishers would like to thank the*
*following for permission to reproduce*
*photographs:*

Camera Press, Fox Photos Ltd, Frank
Spooner Pictures, Keystone Press
Agency, Rex Features, Syndication
International.

Printed in Great Britain at the
University Press, Oxford

# To the teacher

*Workbook B* of *Streamline English Destinations* consists of forty units. Each unit relates directly to the equivalent unit in *Streamline English Destinations* Units 41–80.

The *Workbook* is an optional element of the course, designed to provide language summaries and additional written exercises. It may be used in the following ways:

1   In more extensive courses as additional classroom material, providing extra oral practice and written reinforcement and consolidation of the basic core material in the student's edition.

2   As material for homework in more intensive situations.

The *Workbook* should only be used after full oral practice of the corresponding unit in the student's edition. The language summaries provide material for revision.

A workbook is also available for units 1–40 of the student's edition, under the title *Workbook A.*

*Bernard Hartley*
*Peter Viney*

# Unit 41

## Exercise 1

Read these instructions for making a traditional English cup of tea, and number them 1–6 in the correct order.

Wait for five minutes to let the tea brew.

Make sure the water is boiling vigorously and fill the teapot. Always take the pot to the kettle and not the kettle to the pot.

Put in one teaspoonful of tea per person plus one extra teaspoonful (one for the pot).

Fill a kettle with fresh water and boil it.

When it is nearly boiling put a little of the hot water into a teapot. Whirl it round to warm the pot and throw it away.

Serve with cold milk and sugar to taste.

## Exercise 2

Read the recipe for Shepherd's Pie. Write out a recipe from your region or country in the same way.

---

### SHEPHERD'S PIE

*(For 4 people )*

*Ingredients*

| | |
|---|---|
| 500g potatoes | cooking oil or fat |
| salt and pepper | 1 teaspoon mixed herbs |
| 1 tablespoon milk | 500g minced beef or lamb |
| 15g butter | 200ml beef stock |
| 1 onion, chopped | |

Cook the potatoes in boiling salted water for 20 minutes. Drain. Mash with the milk, butter and salt and pepper. Heat the oil or fat in a saucepan and fry the onion gently until softened (5 minutes). Stir in the minced meat and allow it to brown. Add herbs, stock and salt and pepper. Put mixture in an ovenproof dish. Spread the potato on top. Bake in an oven pre-heated to 180°C for 30 minutes. Remove. Place under a hot grill until the top is crisp and brown.

---

## Exercise 3

Make a list of twenty items (not food or drink) which you might find in a kitchen.

1 ......................................
2 ......................................
3 ......................................
4 ......................................
5 ......................................
6 ......................................
7 ......................................
8 ......................................
9 ......................................
10 ......................................

11 ......................................
12 ......................................
13 ......................................
14 ......................................
15 ......................................
16 ......................................
17 ......................................
18 ......................................
19 ......................................
20 ......................................

## Exercise 4

You have been offered a four course meal. You can have anything you want. Write out the menu you would choose.

1st course ..................................................................

....................................................................................

2nd course ..................................................................

....................................................................................

3rd course ..................................................................

....................................................................................

4th course ..................................................................

....................................................................................

## Exercise 5

Ask a friend these questions, and write down his/her answers.

1 What time do you usually have

  **A** breakfast? ..............................................................

  **B** lunch? ....................................................................

  **C** your evening meal? ...............................................

2 Which is your biggest meal of the day?

  ....................................................................................

3 Do you ever have snacks between meals?

....................................................................................

4 Is there anything that you really cannot eat or drink?

....................................................................................

5 What's your favourite food?

....................................................................................

## Exercise 6

Make a list of *everything* that you ate and drank yesterday. Compare your list with a friend's list.

# Unit 42

## Language summary

| I wish I | was there. |
| --- | --- |
| | wasn't here. |
| | was working there. |
| | wasn't working here. |
| | had ____ a car. |
| | didn't have |
| | didn't have (to do it). |

| I wish I | I could (do it). |
| --- | --- |
| | 'd (done it). |
| | had |
| | hadn't |
| | worked there. |
| | didn't work here. |

## Exercise 1

Gary is 19. He's just read about Rick Faber in the newspaper.

This is Rick Faber.    *I wish I was Rick Faber.*

Write more sentences.

1  He's a millionaire.
2  He's been to 80 countries.
3  He lives in Switzerland.
4  He's got houses in London and New York.
5  He can run five miles.
6  He's getting married to Jaqui Wall.

## Exercise 2

Read the article about Rick Faber again. Write five sentences for Gary, beginning 'I wish ...'

1  rock star
2  19 million selling LPs
3  sing and dance for three hours
4  six cars
5  a Ferrari

## Exercise 3

Gary asked three people this question:
*'Do you wish you were a millionaire?'*
One said, *'Yes, I do'*. Another said, *'No, I don't'*. The third said, *'I am a millionaire!'*

Look at Exercises 1 and 2. Write six questions, and give *true* answers.

### Nigel Wimpster's
### *Personality Page*
Daily Post

**A birthday present for the man who has everything!**

What do you give to a man who has everything? Millionaire rock-star Rick Faber celebrated his 38th birthday last week. Rick, who sings with 'The Tumbling Dice' rock group, has been one of the world's most popular rock artists for nearly 20 years. During that time, he's been to more than 80 different countries and has made 19 million-selling LP records.

Rick lives in Switzerland, but also maintains houses in London and New York. He can still sing and dance throughout the group's 3 hour stage show, and keeps fit by jogging. He can run 5 miles before breakfast everyday! Next month he's getting married to top American model Jaqui Wall. She must have thought for a long time about his birthday present. After all, he owns 6 cars, and usually drives a Ferrari. Her present was certainly different. She gave him a pair of pet leopards!

## Exercise 4

Rick Faber was interviewed by BBC Radio for the 'Rock Review' programme recently. These are some of the things he said:

1  'I'd like to be 19 again!'
2  'I have to travel all the time. I don't like it.'
3  'I get bored singing the same songs all the time.'
4  'I'm getting married to Jaqui. She's very beautiful, but she bores me.'
5  'I'm sorry that I can't live in England, but taxes are too high for me.'
6  'I'm fed up with living abroad.'
7  'I'm tired of being a rock star.'
8  'I'm fed up with having lots of money.'
9  'I hate running – but I have to keep fit for the stage shows.'
10  'I don't like having six cars. I'd like to travel on an ordinary London bus, but I'm too famous.'
11  'When I was 19, I could have got a job in a bank, married the girl next door, and bought a nice little house. I'm sorry I didn't. I think I would have been happier.'

Look at the things Rick said.

*He wishes he was 19 again.*
*He wishes he didn't have to travel.*

Now write eleven sentences with 'wish' like the examples.

## Exercise 5

Look at the Language summary. Write down eight things that *you* wish.

# Unit 43

*I wish they | had | done it.*
          | *hadn't* |

*I'm sorry it happened.*
*I regret | it.*
       | *doing it.*

*If I'd done this, that would have happened.*

*My only regret is . . .*

---

### Exercise 1

Look at the list of school subjects. Think about the previous school year *or* when you were at school. Put ticks in the boxes next to the subjects you studied.

### SCHOOL SUBJECTS

| | | | |
|---|---|---|---|
| Typing | | Greek | |
| Shorthand | | A 2nd foreign language | |
| Cookery | | Computer studies | |
| Woodwork | | Sociology | |
| Metalwork | | Biology | |
| Household electrics | | Chemistry | |
| Needlework | | Political studies | |
| Latin | | | |

### Exercise 2

Look at these examples.

*I wish I hadn't studied Latin.*
or *I'm glad I studied Latin.*
or *I wish I'd studied Latin.*
or *I'm glad I didn't study Latin.*

Write true sentences about the subjects in the list.

### Exercise 3

Look at these four sentences.

**A** *I wish I hadn't studied Latin because it was boring, and I'll never have to use it.*
**B** *I'm glad I studied Latin because it has helped me to study other languages.*
**C** *I wish I'd studied Latin. It would have been useful for university entrance.*
**D** *I'm glad I didn't study Latin. I think it would have been a waste of time.*

Look at the sentences you wrote in Exercise 2. Choose six, write them out again, adding reasons.

### Exercise 4

I bought a calculator. It didn't work.
*I wish I hadn't bought it.*

Continue.

**1** My friends went to London. I didn't go.

.......................................................................

**2** I failed the examination.

.......................................................................

**3** I was very rude to her yesterday.

.......................................................................

**4** I never played games at school.

.......................................................................

**5** I had to wear a uniform to school.

.......................................................................

**6** I chose the wrong job.

.......................................................................

### Exercise 5

I bought a calculator. It didn't work.   *I regret buying it.*

Look at Exercise 4. Write six sentences, with 'I regret (doing) . . .' or 'I regret not (doing) . . .'

### Exercise 6

Think about the last year. Write three sentences with 'I regret doing . . .', three with 'I don't regret doing . . .', and three with 'I'm sorry I did . . .'.

### Exercise 7

I'm very tired today.   *I wish I wasn't.*
I went to bed late last night.   *I wish I hadn't.*

Respond to the following sentences in the same way.

**1** I didn't set the alarm.

.......................................................................

**2** It didn't go off.

.......................................................................

**3** I arrived late.

.......................................................................

**4** Now, I can't concentrate on my work.

.......................................................................

**5** I feel terrible!

.......................................................................

**6** I don't understand anything.

.......................................................................

**7** I'm bored.

.......................................................................

# Unit 44

## Exercise 1

Read the three letters, and complete the chart.

| Name | Childhood ambition | Childhood hobbies | Present occupation | Present hobbies | Ambition now |
|---|---|---|---|---|---|
| Annabel Chambers | | | | | |
| Howard Skinner | | | | | |
| Tim Cleveland | | | | | |

# READERS' LETTERS

*Last month we asked our readers to tell us about their ambitions and dreams. Lots of you wrote in! Here are three of your letters.*

*Annabel Chambers*

*Howard Skinner*

*Tim Cleveland*

**They say that every small child** wants to be an engine driver. I suppose that might have been true in the days of steam trains, but it's pretty difficult to get excited about an electric train. Personally, I always wanted to be a pilot. I used to spend hours at the local airport with my brother, writing down the plane registrations. I knew everything there was to know about planes! When I was twelve I began to realize that the thick glasses I had to wear would make that ambition impossible. It's always a shock when you first realize that wishes don't always come true! It's funny. I really can't stand flying now. I often have to travel in my job... I'm a fashion buyer... and I suppose I've got fed up with flying. I'm still a collector, but now it's china ornaments, not plane registrations. I think I've become something of an expert on 19th century English china. I'd really like to write a book about it. I think that would be my biggest ambition!

*Annabel Chambers*

**When I was a kid** I just had one dream. I used to imagine myself running out onto the field at Wembley Stadium, a football under my arm... the captain of the England team! I'd spend hours kicking a ball against the wall. I used to collect autographs too. I'd hang around before a match and try and get the players to sign a programme when they got out of their cars. Programmes! That's another thing. My bedroom was full of dusty football programmes. I used to swop them with other kids at school. I work in a shoe shop now. All the little kids come in with their mums and dads, trying on football boots. They get so excited. I can remember doing the same thing. I've lost interest in football nowadays. I prefer messing around in my workshop. I've built a nice little workshop in the garage. I make children's toys. You know, wooden ones. I really wish I could do it for a living... full-time. Still, perhaps one day I'll be able to.

*Howard Skinner*

**When I was about seven,** a travelling circus came to our town and I still remember what a strong impression it made on me. I loved all the characters I saw and I had dreamt of running away to join them. I seriously considered all the possibilities; lion tamer, elephant boy, acrobat, trapeze artist, but in the end I decided to be a clown. I can remember spending long hours at my mother's dressing-table, putting on make-up to create a clown's face and then pulling faces in front of the mirror. Unfortunately I never ran away to join the circus. I left school at 15, did an apprenticeship and now work as a mechanic in a large garage – I suppose that's a bit of a circus sometimes! I'd like my own place one day; nothing big, just to be my own boss. At weekends I like to get away from everything. I spend hours and hours just sitting by a river or a lake, just watching my float. I don't really mind if I don't catch anything, though I get a big thrill if I do! As soon as I could walk, my father used to take me with him, made me a rod, and I suppose that's how I've spent my spare time ever since.

*Tim Cleveland*

## Exercise 2

Write a paragraph about your childhood hobbies and ambitions, and your hobbies and ambitions now.

# Unit 45

**Language summary**

| He<br>She | is the one | who<br>that | does<br>did | it. | | He's<br>She's<br>It's | the one. I saw | him.<br>her.<br>it. |
|---|---|---|---|---|---|---|---|---|
| It<br>That | | which<br>that | | | | They're | the ones. I saw | them. |
| Those<br>They're | are the ones | who<br>which<br>that | do<br>did | | | He's<br>She's<br>It's | the one I saw. | |
| | | | | | | They're | the ones I saw. | |

Lord Street is a small side-street in Watermouth. Look at the six shops.

One of them sells confectionery and tobacco.
One of them repairs shoes.
One of them does dry cleaning.

One of them sells antiques.
One of them does photo-copying.
One of them sells children's clothes.

## Exercise 1

*'Bygones' must be the one that sells antiques.*

Write five more sentences.

## Exercise 2

Antique shop/Copy-shop/Tobacconist's/Cobbler's/Dry Cleaner's/Children's Boutique
*A shop which sells children's clothes is a Children's Boutique.*

Write five more sentences.

## Exercise 3

Look at these statements by the people who run (own or manage) the shops.

**Donald Swain** 'I visit all the auctions, and I advertise in the local paper. It's a hobby as well as a job.'

**William Smart** 'We bought the shop when I retired. I like working with my wife, and it's nice to meet so many people. I don't smoke myself, which is strange, I suppose.'

**Antonia Porter** 'I've got three children, and it was so difficult to find nice clothes for them. That's why I decided to start my own business.'

**Sylvia Openshaw** 'Actually, I'm not the owner. It's a national chain, and I'm just the manageress. We do it all on the premises. If you bring in something at ten, it'll be ready by twelve.'

**Penelope Rankin** 'I used to teach secretarial skills. So many offices have rotten equipment. The machines here are terribly expensive, but I lease them from the manufacturer.'

**Percival Digby** 'Forty years in the trade, that's me. Of course the quality's gone down a lot ... all these synthetics. If you ask me, leather's still the best.'

*William Smart must be the one that runs 'W & E Smart'.*
Write five more sentences.

## Exercise 4

*William Smart is the man who runs the shop which sells confectionery and tobacco.*
Write five more sentences.

## Exercise 5

Look at the statements in Exercise 3.

*William Smart is the man who bought a shop when he retired.*
*He's the one who works with his wife.*
Write ten more sentences.

## Exercise 6

That's the club. I went to it last night.     *That's the club I went to last night.*
Continue.

1 That's the hotel. I've often stayed in it. ...........................

..................................................................................

2 This is the book. I'm reading it at the moment. ................

..................................................................................

3 She's the woman. I gave the documents to her. ............

..................................................................................

4 Those are the girls. My sister teaches them. ...................

..................................................................................

5 These are the letters. You asked me to post them. .........

..................................................................................

6 He must be the boy. We saw him running away. ............

..................................................................................

7 This is the magazine. I told you about it. .......................

..................................................................................

8 These must be the ones. You wanted me to find them.

..................................................................................

## Exercise 7

That's the shop. It sells antiques.     *That's the shop which sells antiques.*
That's the shop. I was in it this morning.     *That's the shop I was in this morning.*
Continue.

1 She's the one. I used to be at school with her. ...............

..................................................................................

2 She's the one. She used to be at school with me. ..........

..................................................................................

3 He's the man. He plays for Eastfield United. ...................

..................................................................................

4 He's the man. I've often seen him on TV. ......................

..................................................................................

5 They're the people. They live in my street. ....................

..................................................................................

6 They're the people. I live near them. .............................

..................................................................................

7 Those are the ones. I've been looking for them. ............

..................................................................................

8 Those must be the ones. They were on my desk. ..........

..................................................................................

# Unit 46

**Language summary**

He went to Scotland WHERE he did this.
This is WHERE it happened.

He was looking for someone WHOSE uniform he could steal.
A girl, WHOSE hands were tied, was lying beside him.

## SEVEN DAYS IN ENGLAND BY COACH

**Anglo ▷ tours**

**PRICE INCLUDES BREAKFAST AND EVENING MEAL**

*ITINERARY*

*Day one*

**LONDON**
visit Tower of London &
Buckingham Palace
*evening,* Jupiter Club – cabaret
*overnight:* Upminster Hotel

*Day two*

**CAMBRIDGE**
go round colleges
*evening* in a country pub
–country dancing
*overnight* : University Arms Hotel

*Day three*

**STRATFORD-ON-AVON**
sightseeing
*evening,* theatre visit–'Romeo and Juliet'
*overnight:* Falstaff Hotel

*Day four*

**OXFORD**
visit University
*evening,* Tudor Restaurant–special dinner
*overnight:* Hotel Academia

*Day five*

**NEW FOREST & BOURNEMOUTH**
see Winchester Cathedral
*afternoon,* Beaulieu National
Motor Museum
*overnight;* Continental Hotel, Bournemouth

*Day six*

**BATH**
see Roman Baths
*evening,* country pub–folksinging
*overnight:* Hotel Trajan

*Day seven*

**LONDON**
shopping, West End
*evening,* National Theatre–'Hamlet'
*overnight:* Airport Hotel

## Exercise 1

The tour starts on Tuesday. A travel agent is telling a customer about it.

Day 1
**A** *On Tuesday we're going to London where we'll visit the Tower and Buckingham Palace.*
**B** *In the evening we're going to the Jupiter Club where we'll see a cabaret.*

Now write the programme for Days 2, 3, 4, 5, 6 and 7.

## Exercise 2

The courier and the driver are discussing their last tour, and some of the things that happened.

Paul Muller/passport was stolen/in Cambridge.

**Driver** *Do you remember Paul Muller?*
**Courier** *Yes, I do. He's the man whose passport was stolen in Cambridge.*

Write sentences with 'whose'.

1 Martha Van Buren/husband danced on the table at the Jupiter Club.
2 Mr and Mrs Rossi/little boy was sick on the coach in Oxford.
3 Madame Le Brun/suitcase broke at the airport.
4 Señor Gonzalez/wallet was stolen in London.
5 Mr Davies/wife got drunk in Bournemouth.
6 Mr and Mrs Macdonald/daughter got engaged to a waiter in Bath.

## Exercise 3

That's the club. Mr Van Buren danced on the table there.
*That's the club where Mr Van Buren danced on the table.*

He's the man. His wife didn't speak to him once during the tour.
*He's the man whose wife didn't speak to him once during the tour.*

Join these sentences in the same way.

1 This is a picture of the Hotel Academia. We stayed there in Oxford.
2 Madame Le Brun was the woman. Her suitcase was full of bottles of whisky.
3 Bath was the place! Mr Macdonald punched a waiter there.
4 This is a picture of Beaulieu. The National Motor Museum is situated there.
5 Do you remember Mr and Mrs Rossi? Their son was sick three times.
6 Mr Davies was the man. His wife drank 1½ litres of wine.
7 Winchester Cathedral was the place. Paul Muller broke his camera there.
8 She's the lady. Her husband was always late for the bus.
9 Mrs Macdonald's the one. Her husband fell asleep during 'Hamlet'.
10 Do you remember that pub near Cambridge? Señor Gonzalez sang some songs in Spanish there.

# Unit 47

**Language summary**

*This is the place* WHERE *it happened.*
*That's the day* WHEN *it happened.*
*He's the man* WHO *did it.*

*It's the thing* WHICH *did it.*
*She's the one* WHOSE *friend did it.*

## Exercise 1

Read this passage and complete the spaces with: where/when/who/which/whose.

**"Remember, remember the fifth of November, gunpowder, treason and plot ..."**

The 5th of November is a day ................... children all over Britain light bonfires

and set off fireworks. They are remembering Guy Fawkes ................... attempt

to blow up the Houses of Parliament was unsuccessful in 1605. On November

4th, Fawkes was found hiding in the cellars ................... lie beneath Parliament.

There was also a large quantity of gunpowder ................... he intended to set

off ................... the King opened the new session of Parliament the next day.

He was arrested, sentenced to death and hanged. There were several others in

the plot, but Fawkes was the one ................... was caught and blamed. If he

had succeeded, he would have killed the King, all of the Bishops, a large

percentage of the aristocracy and most of the Members of Parliament. The

cellars ................... Fawkes was captured are still searched before each

opening of Parliament, and on the evening of November 4th every year.

November 5th is known as 'Guy Fawkes' Night', and a model of Fawkes is

burned on the bonfires. Unfortunately, November 5th is also an evening

................... hospitals are very busy treating children ................... have been

injured by fireworks. The fire brigade is also busy, putting out the fires

................... have been started accidentally. Some people believe that it is a

festival ................... we should forget. There are now strict controls on shops

................... children buy fireworks, and television warnings about the dangers of

fireworks.

## Exercise 2

optician/tests people's eyes   *A person who tests people's eyes is an optician.*
bank/cash cheques   *A place where you can cash cheques is a bank.*
November 5th/Guy Fawkes   *November 5th is the day when we remember Guy Fawkes.*
vacuum cleaner/cleans carpets   *A machine which cleans carpets is a vacuum cleaner.*
orphan/parents dead   *A child whose parents are dead is an orphan.*

Now write sentences from these prompts.

1 lawn mower/cuts grass ...................................
.....................................................

2 November 11th/end of World War I ...........................
.....................................................

3 vet/treats sick animals .................................
.....................................................

4 building society/borrow money to buy a house ...............
.....................................................

5 widower/wife dead .....................................
.....................................................

6 record player/plays records .............................
.....................................................

7 journalist/writes for newspapers ..........................
.....................................................

8 July 14th/the French Revolution ...........................
.....................................................

9 filling station/buy petrol ...............................

10 video recorder/records television programmes ............

11 gymnasium/do exercises ................................
.....................................................

12 widow/husband dead ..................................
.....................................................

13 waiter/brings your food in a restaurant .....................
.....................................................

14 April 23rd/St George, the patron saint of England ........
.....................................................

# Unit 48

**Look at this**

Robert Gibbs has been recaptured! (He escaped from prison last Friday.)
*Robert Gibbs, who escaped from prison last Friday, has been recaptured.*

A 3-year-old block of flats is going to be demolished! (It cost £10 million.)
*A 3-year-old block of flats, which cost £10 million, is going to be demolished.*

Brian Huff, the Eastfield Manager, has been sacked! (The crowd booed him from the field last Saturday.)
*Brian Huff, the Eastfield Manager, who the crowd booed from the field last Saturday, has been sacked.*

The Lanstable self-portrait has been sold for £900,000! (He painted it from his death bed.)
*The Lanstable self-portrait, which he painted from his death bed, has been sold for £900,000.*

Jim Miles, the racing driver, will never race again! (His legs were badly injured in last year's Grand Prix crash.)
*Jim Miles, the racing driver, whose legs were badly injured in last year's Grand Prix crash, will never race again.*

The British Motors Calypso is now Britain's best-selling car! (Its success surprised everybody.)
*The British Motors Calypso, whose success surprised everybody, is now Britain's best-selling car.*

## Exercise 1

Study the 'Look at this' section above and then read the following passage.
Some commas have been removed from the passage. Replace them.

### Heathrow hijack

A vanload of silver bullion which is estimated to be worth £5,000,000 was hijacked in broad daylight yesterday. The bullion van which was approaching Heathrow Airport was waved into a lay-by by two men on the A3044. The men who were armed were both dressed in police uniforms. The driver and the security guard who also had guns were asked to step down and present their driving documents. They were then attacked and overpowered by a number of men. The men had been hiding in another van in the lay-by. Both vans then drove away, taking the security guards who the thieves had tied up with them. The security van was later found abandoned. The two guards whose hands were still tied were inside the van. The police uniforms which the thieves had rented from a theatrical supplier were on the front seats. The bullion which was being transported from the City to the airport was in kilo bars. The two guards whose injuries were not serious are being questioned by detectives.

## Exercise 2

Study the 'Look at this' section. Connect these sentences in the same way.

**1** Trevor Franklin has broken his leg. (He plays for Eastfield United.)

..................................................................................................................................................

**2** The new 'Tumbling Dice' LP has already sold one million copies. (It was recorded in Jamaica.)

..................................................................................................................................................

**3** Carl Haigh has won the Nobel Prize for Science. (Michael Parkhurst interviewed him on TV last week.)

..................................................................................................................................................

**4** The racehorse 'White Rum' was sold for £3 million yesterday. (Gordon Lester rode it in the Hampshire Gold Cup.)

..................................................................................................................................................

**5** Jason Douglas will be the star of the new Hollywood Film 'Juke Box '58'. (His last film won an Academy Award.)

..................................................................................................................................................

**6** The M31 motorway will be opened by the Queen on Friday. (It has taken four years to build.)

..................................................................................................................................................

**7** Laura Evans is retiring from international tennis. (Doreen Waters beat her in the women's final at Wimbledon.)

..................................................................................................................................................

**8** An antique table has been auctioned for £20,000. (Chippenham made it in 1743).

..................................................................................................................................................

**9** Max Millwall gave his last performance on Saturday. (He first became a comedian forty years ago.)

..................................................................................................................................................

# Unit 49

## Language summary

| ... to/for/from/on/in/about/of | | which ... |
| ... all | of | whom ... |
| ... one | | |
| ... some | | |
| ... two | | |
| ... none | | |

Formal, written style
*He was the man to whom I spoke.*

Spoken and informal written style
*He was the man* | *I spoke to.*
| *who I spoke to.*
| *that I spoke to.*

Formal style
*Mr Lazenby, to whom I addressed it, replied in a most unsatisfactory way.*

Informal style
*Mr Lazenby, who I addressed it to, replied in a most unsatisfactory way.*

## Exercise 1

Mrs Daniels has just received this letter from the Sleeptight Bedding Company. Copy it out as a formal letter, with capital letters and correct punctuation.

> sleeptight bedding company 115 down street duckbury wiltshire 13th october mrs k daniels 82 glendower road cardiff CF3 8BJ dear mrs daniels we acknowledge receipt of your order for a 'mallard' continental quilt and cover if the goods are not received within 28 days please contact us quoting our reference KD73/5/10 yours rosemary loakes (miss) despatch manager

## Exercise 2

I took it back to the shop I had bought it from.
*I took it back to the shop from which I had bought it.*

Write these sentences in a more formal style.

1 Miss Henley is the secretary I spoke to on the telephone.
2 Continental Computers is the company he invested all his money in.
3 Preston is the Lancashire town I saw a documentary about.
4 Wibanya is a country I know nothing about.
5 The XL5000 is the micro-computer I paid £1000 for.
6 Appletree Farm is the land we are going to build the new factory on.
7 You wrote to Mr Wall, who I am replying for.
8 Herbert Thomas is the man who I got your address from.
9 Our Head Office is the place enquiries should be sent to.
10 I am sure you wish to protect your company's good name, which you must be proud of.

## Exercise 3

We tried several garages. None of them had the parts in stock.
*We tried several garages, none of which had the parts in stock.*

Join these sentences in the same way.

1 I spoke to two counter assistants. One of them was extremely rude.
2 We bought two batteries. Neither of them worked.
3 We have employed many temporary secretaries from your agency. Most of them were reliable and efficient.
4 We have several holiday flats vacant in June. All of them are equipped to the highest standards.
5 There are 20,000 fans at Eastfield United. Only a few of them misbehave at matches.
6 There are eight candidates. Three of them are very well-qualified.
7 We bought 2000 light bulbs from your company. Many of them have since proved to be faulty.
8 We spoke to two of your representatives. Both of them refused to comment.
9 There are 600 students. The majority of them are Spanish speakers.
10 We received 30,000 roof tiles. About 10% of them were cracked on delivery.

## Exercise 4

Mrs Jackson no longer lives here. (You addressed the letter to her.)
*Mrs Jackson, to whom you addressed the letter, no longer lives here.*

Join these sentences in the same way.

1 The bank counter was covered with black ink. (I placed my new handbag on it.)
2 Jason Douglas will be opening the exhibition. (You must have heard of him.)
3 Mr Grant asked me to contact you. (I was speaking with him yesterday.)
4 Walters and Co. would like more information about your products. (We are acting for them as agents.)
5 The 'Calypso' is still not available in this area. (We have been hearing a lot about it recently.)
6 The 'Daily Post' advised me to go to the police. (I saw your advertisement in it.)
7 Mrs Dundalk will supply references. (I was employed by her until last week.)

# Unit 50

## Thomas HOLIDAYS

## HOTEL GUIDE

All prices shown include continental breakfast

| Star rating | Hotel | | | Location | Price |
|---|---|---|---|---|---|
| ★★ | APOLLO | 60 rooms | (30 sea view) | Benitses, Corfu | £200 |
| ★★★ | EL CID | 300 rooms | (200 with balcony) | Palma, Majorca | £220 |
| ★★★★ | LEONARDO | 120 rooms | (All sea view) | Rimini, Italy | £250 |
| ★★★★★ | VOLTAIRE | 212 rooms | (90 sea view, All colour TV) | Nice, France | £300 |

### Exercise 1

Look at the sentences about the 'Apollo'. Write similar ones about the 'El Cid'.

The Apollo

1 *It's the one that's in Corfu.*
2 *It's the one that's in Benitses.*
3 *It's the only one that's got two stars.*
4 *It's the one that costs £200.*
5 *The Apollo, which is in Corfu, is a two-star hotel.*
6 *The Apollo, which is a two-star hotel, is in Benitses.*
7 *The Apollo, which is in Benitses, costs £200.*
8 *The Apollo, which costs £200, has got two stars.*
9 *The Apollo has 60 rooms, 30 of which have a sea view.*
10 *At the Apollo there will be a courier who speaks fluent Greek.*

### Exercise 2

Read this paragraph about the 'Leonardo', and write a similar one about the 'Voltaire'.

The Leonardo

*The Leonardo, which overlooks the beach at Rimini, is a four-star hotel. It is the only four-star hotel which we offer in this area. It has 120 rooms, all of which have a sea view. The price of the holiday is £250, which includes continental breakfast. At the hotel there will be a courier who speaks fluent Italian.*

A SONG for EUROPE

The Eurovision Song Contest is an annual competition. European countries enter a singer or group with a new song for the contest, and panels in each country vote for the best song. Here are the results of a recent contest.

| POSITION | COUNTRY | ARTIST | SONG TITLE | COMPOSER | VOTES |
|---|---|---|---|---|---|
| 1. | Italy | Maria and Paula | 'Ciao Milano' | Franco Benedetti | 187 |
| 2. | United Kingdom | The Shining Teeth | 'Wam, bam, Boom' | Jeff Keats | 182 |
| 3. | Spain | Jesus Perez | 'Viva Costa Brava' | Osvaldo Villa | 179 |
| 4. | Ireland | Bridget O'Toole | 'The Green Hills of Home' | Bridget O'Toole | 177 |

### Exercise 3

Look at these sentences and write similar ones about each of the other artists.

Maria and Paula
1 *Maria and Paula are the ones that came first.*
2 *They're the ones that sang 'Ciao, Milano'.*
3 *Maria and Paula, who come from Italy, got 187 votes.*
4 *Maria and Paula, who got 187 votes, came first.*
5 *Maria and Paula, whose song was written by Franco Benedetti, came first.*

# Unit 51

## Under £20 Page

### EVERY MONDAY IN YOUR 'EVENING ECHO'

**CLOAK** black, hooded, full-length, lined. Italian made, ideal for fancy dress parties. £19·99 – 707409.

**BEAUTIFUL** ladies' ankle boots, fringed, red, size 6. Purchased Paris boxed, unworn, bargain £12 – 476358.

**RADIOMOBILE** push-button car radio with speaker, v.g.c. £15 – 523564

**WHITE** cast-iron bath, turquoise panels, taps with shower. £15 o.n.o. – 22641.

**GIRLS** dark red winter coat, detachable hood. 1.32 in, £8. Also blue belted-style coat £8. – 423346.

**VICIOUS** Alsatian guard dog barking ferociously on tape cassette. Great deterrent to intruders. £1.85 – 733555 Evenings.

**DRESSING table.** Modern, ideal child's room, light oak, two deep drawers, long dressing mirror, new cond. £14 – 476139.

**TABLE** 42 in×21 in blue formica top complete with two chairs. Hardly used £15 – 684139 after 6 p.m.

**PRAM** navy blue detachable body and shopping tray. As new £19·50 Tel. 423340.

**HOOVER** junior vacuum cleaner incl. accessories. Little used £18 – 707147.

**T.V.** B/W portable 12 in. Good picture. V. reasonable at £19 – 27414.

**RECORD** player – stereo. Scarcely used. Unwanted gift. £15 – 513470.

**CAMERA** – Kodak instamatic, built-in flash, unused £12 – 642879.

**CHILDREN'S** encyclopedia, 8 vols, hardly ever opened. £13·50 – 523242.

**GIRLS'** brown fur coat, with cream coloured trim. Age 8-9 yrs. Length 34in. v.g.c. worn once £8 – 284329

**PAIR** curtains. Regency stripe, brown/cream/gold. Length 54in ×70in. Width. £19·99 – 769107

**TYPEWRITER** – portable, new ribbon, recently overhauled. Excel. cond. Bargain £16 – 729753.

**BRAND-new** men's black size 10 Wellington boots. Unused. £4 – Tel. 79665 after 6 p.m.

**MEN'S** charcoal grey, all wool overcoat. Size 42 chest. £19·95 – 25090

**SEWING MACHINE,** Singer. Modern, electric, automatic, many attachments, working order. £19·50 – 623487

---

### Exercise 1

Find abbreviations which mean:

1. black and white
2. years
3. very good condition
4. excellent
5. volumes
6. telephone
7. inches
8. or near offer
9. including
10. very
11. new condition
12. length

### Exercise 2

There are nine expressions which mean 'new' or 'nearly new'. What are they?

### Exercise 3

1. List the items of clothing which are advertised.
2. List the manufacturer's names in the advertisements.

### Exercise 4

Imagine that you wish to sell one of your possessions for less than £20. Complete this coupon.

### Exercise 5

Now write four similar advertisements for four more of your possessions.

### Exercise 6

Describing things in an advertisement is rather different from descriptions in a more formal text. Look at the table in Unit 51 of the Student's Book.

He's got a .............. car. (French, old, rusty, dirty)
*He's got a dirty old rusty French car.*

Rewrite these sentences, putting the adjectives in the most appropriate order.

1. It's a .............. painting. (landscape, valuable, 18th century)
2. She lives in a .............. flat. (three-bedroomed, spacious, studio)
3. I've just bought a .............. briefcase. (leather, brown, smart)
4. I'd like .............. eggs. (dozen, two, fresh, brown, large)
5. He's got an .............. recorder. (Japanese, video, expensive, portable)
6. Look at those .............. figures. (antique, porcelain, French)
7. I'm looking for a .............. pullover. (V-neck, green, machine-washable, lambswool)
8. I was bitten by a .............. dog. (black, huge, Alsatian, savage)
9. She drives a .............. car. (blue, Fiat, light, little, lovely)

# Unit 52

| | | | |
|---|---|---|---|
| **A** Charles Orson | **E** Igor Romanoff | **H** Dick Harris | **K** Lou Fox |
| **B** Terry Saville | **F** Federico Cortina | **I** Sheena Gray | **L** Roland |
| **C** Beth Davies | **G** Chloe Jackson | **J** Sylvie Horne | J. Frankfurter |
| **D** Bobo Malik | | | **M** Doreen Barker |

## Exercise 1

**A** *Who's the short fat man with a bald head and glasses?*
**B** *That's Charles Orson.*

Continue.

**1 A** ................................................................

................................................................

  **B** ................................................................

**2 A** ................................................................

................................................................

  **B** ................................................................

**3 A** ................................................................

................................................................

  **B** ................................................................

**4 A** ................................................................

................................................................

  **B** ................................................................

**5 A** ................................................................

................................................................

  **B** ................................................................

**6 A** ................................................................

................................................................

  **B** ................................................................

**7 A** ................................................................

................................................................

  **B** ................................................................

**8 A** ................................................................

................................................................

  **B** ................................................................

**9 A** ........................................................
........................................................
**B** ........................................................
**10 A** ........................................................
........................................................
**B** ........................................................

**11 A** ........................................................
........................................................
**B** ........................................................
**12 A** ........................................................
........................................................
**B** ........................................................

## Exercise 2

Write a short description of a student in your class. Read it out.
See if the other students can guess who it is.

## Exercise 3

Look at the example and complete the table.

| *The man who has got a bald head.* | *The man with a bald head.* | *The bald-headed man.* |
|---|---|---|
| The girl who has got blue eyes. | .................................... .................................... | .................................... .................................... |
| .................................... .................................... | The man with grey hair. | .................................... .................................... |
| .................................... .................................... | .................................... .................................... | The bearded man. |
| The woman who has got thin lips. | .................................... .................................... | .................................... .................................... |

## Exercise 4

Write brief descriptions of these people.

**1**

**2**

**3**

**4**

**5**

**6**

# Unit 53

### Language summary

*He (did this) to (do that).*
*He sent (someone) to (do that).*

*He (did this)* │ *so as to* │ *(do that).*
              │ *in order to* │

*So as to* │ *(do that), he (did this).*
*In order to* │

### A hard luck story

It was a bit of bad luck when the motorist broke down – he was stuck on double yellow lines. So he went into a store to borrow a pen and paper to leave a note for the traffic warden. The pen, however, was like his car. It didn't work. When he decided to go back to the store to buy a pen, he found another little difficulty. He had only a £20 note and the salesgirl couldn't change it. So he set off to find a bank to change the note to buy the pen to write on the paper to put on his car to tell the traffic warden that his car had broken down. As he left the bank he spotted a phone box. He decided to call a garage to send a truck to tow the car away, but the number was engaged. When he got back to his car he found a parking ticket on the windscreen. The story has, however, a happy ending. The driver wrote to the head of the local police force to explain what had happened. The police superintendent who read the letter decided to let him off the £10 parking fine. He said that even if the man's story was not true, it was so clever that he deserved to be let off!

### Exercise 1

Why did he go into a store?
**A** *He went into a store so as to borrow a pen.*
**B** *He went into a store in order to borrow a pen.*

Write two answers to each of these questions.

1 Why did he want to borrow a pen and paper?
2 Why did he decide to go back to the store?
3 Why did he set off to find a bank?
4 Why did he want to leave a note on the car?
5 Why did he want the garage to send a truck?
6 Why did he write to the head of the local police force?

### Exercise 2

She employed a secretary ⎰ *to answer the phone.*
                         ⎱ *to help with her work.*
                         ⎱ *to type her letters.*
                         ⎱ *or ... something else*

Complete these.

1 He rang for a plumber ..................................................................................................................

2 She phoned an electrician ..........................................................................................................

3 I called a mechanic ......................................................................................................................

4 They commissioned an artist ......................................................................................................

5 We went to a photographer .........................................................................................................

6 She sent him to the optician .......................................................................................................

7 They called the waiter over .........................................................................................................

8 She went to a specialist ...............................................................................................................

9 Lord Worth employed a bodyguard ............................................................................................

10 He bought a savage dog .............................................................................................................

### Exercise 3

Now complete these.

1 She boiled some water ................................................................................................................

2 He smashed the window .............................................................................................................

3 I bought a paper ..........................................................................................................................

4 She used a credit card ................................................................................................................

5 She picked up the receiver .........................................................................................................

6 He took an aspirin .......................................................................................................................

# Unit 54

**Language summary**

| I (did this) | so that | he | could / couldn't | (do that). | or | So that | he | could / couldn't | (do that) | I (did this). |
|---|---|---|---|---|---|---|---|---|---|---|
| | | this | would / wouldn't | (happen). | | | this | would / wouldn't | (happen) | |
| I (do this) ('m doing this) | | he | can / can't | (do that). | | | he | can / can't | (do that) | I (do this). |
| | | this | will / won't | (happen). | | | this | will / won't | (happen) | I'm (doing that) |

*What (is) the purpose of (that)?*

When 006 returned from the Indian Ocean, a new car was waiting for him.
It looked like an ordinary production model but it had a number of extras.

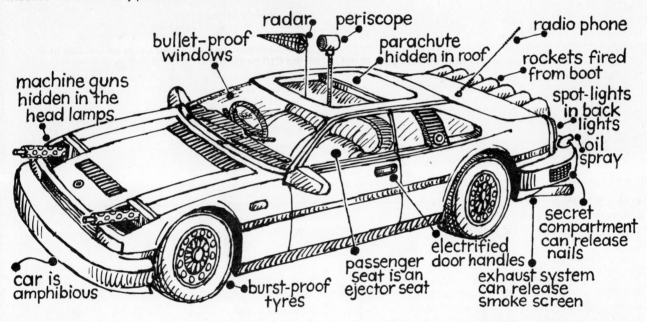

radar  periscope  radio phone

bullet-proof windows  parachute hidden in roof  rockets fired from boot

machine guns hidden in the head lamps  spot-lights in back lights

oil spray

secret compartment can release nails

car is amphibious  burst-proof tyres  passenger seat is an ejector seat  electrified door handles  exhaust system can release smoke screen

## Exercise 1

*There's a periscope so that the car can operate as a submarine.*

Why do you think the other 'extras' have been fitted to the car? Write eleven sentences with 'so that'.

## Exercise 2

*006 was given a false tooth with poison in, so that he could kill himself if he was captured.*

What other things do you think he might have been given, and why? Write three more sentences.

## Exercise 3

Why did he break the window?

*So that he could get into the house.*
or *So that he could get out of the house.*
or *So that he could attract attention.*

**4** Why did he save his money? ........................................

........................................

**5** Why did she fill in the form? ........................................

........................................

Continue.

**1** Why did he grow a beard? ........................................

........................................

**2** Why did she buy a calculator? ........................................

........................................

**3** Why are they learning English? ........................................

........................................

**6** Why did he stop at the garage? ........................................

........................................

**7** Why did she buy some champagne? ........................................

........................................

**8** Why did he buy traveller's cheques? ........................................

# Unit 55

**Language summary**

| Do this | so as<br>in order | not | to do that. |
|---------|-------------------|-----|-------------|
| | to<br>so as to<br>in order to | avoid | that.<br><br>doing that. |
| | to prevent | that.<br>something from happening.<br>somebody from doing that. | |

## WHEN IN THE COUNTRY FOLLOW THE COUNTRY CODE

The Code is a series of ten reminders based on common sense – and common failings. So when in the country remember:

**Guard against all risk of fire**
Plantations, woodlands and heaths are highly inflammable: every year acres burn because of casually dropped matches, cigarette ends or pipe ash

**Fasten all gates**
Even if you found them open. Animals can't be told to stay where they're put. A gate left open invites them to wander, a danger to themselves, to crops and to traffic.

**Keep dogs under proper control**
Farmers have good reason to regard visiting dogs as pests; in the country a civilized town dog can become a savage. Keep your dog on a lead wherever there is livestock about, also on country roads.

**Keep to the paths across farm land**
Crops can be ruined by people's feet. Remember that grass is a valuable crop too, sometimes the only one on the farm. Flattened corn or hay is very difficult to harvest.

**Avoid damaging fences, hedges and walls**
They are expensive items in the farm's economy; repairs are costly and use scarce labour. Keep to the recognized routes, using gates and stiles.

**Leave no litter**
All litter is unsightly, and some is dangerous as well. Take litter home for disposal; in the country it costs a lot to collect it.

**Safeguard water supplies**
Your chosen walk may well cross a catchment area for the water supply of millions. Avoid polluting it in any way. Never interfere with cattle troughs.

**Protect wildlife, wild plants and trees**
Wildlife is best observed, not collected. To pick or uproot flowers, carve trees and rocks. or disturb wild animals and birds, destroys other people's pleasure as well.

**Go carefully on country roads**
Country roads have special dangers: blind corners, high banks and hedges, slow-moving tractors and farm machinery or animals. Motorists should reduce their speed and take extra care; walkers should keep to the right, facing oncoming traffic.

**Respect the life of the countryside**
Set a good example and try to fit in with the life and work of the countryside. This way good relations are preserved, and those who follow are not regarded as enemies.

A booklet, poster, bookmark and children's game showing the Country Code are also available.

## Exercise 1

Find words which mean:

1 an open area of wild, unfarmed land
2 a measure for land (4047 square metres)
3 troublesome or destructive animal or insect
4 agricultural plants in the fields
5 an arrangement of steps to enable people on foot to cross a fence or wall
6 a long open box for animals to feed or drink from

7 a length of rope or leather tied to a dog to control it
8 area from which lakes or rivers get their water
9 to pull a plant, including its roots, from the ground
10 to cut a shape or letters into wood or stone
11 a group word for cows, bulls, etc.
12 cattle, sheep, pigs, goats, etc. kept for use or profit
13 dried grass used to feed animals

## Exercise 2

*You should avoid leaving gates open.*

Write down five other things you should avoid doing in the country.

## Exercise 3

Why shouldn't you drop matches or cigarette ends?
*So as not to start fires.*

Continue.

1 Why shouldn't you leave gates open? ........................

....................

2 Why shouldn't you let your dog run free? ....................

....................

3 Why shouldn't you wander away from paths? ............

....................................................................................

4 Why shouldn't you climb over hedges or fences? .......

....................................................................................

5 Why shouldn't you disturb wildlife? ..............................

....................................................................................

## Exercise 4

Why should you keep your dog on a lead?
*To prevent it from frightening cattle.*

Answer these questions in the same way.

1 Why should you close farm gates?
2 Why shouldn't you drop matches or cigarette ends?

# Unit 56

## Language summary

*The house was* SO *beautiful* THAT *they bought it.*

*He had* SO | *much work*
| *many problems* | THAT *he couldn't sleep at night.*

*They worked* SO *hard* THAT *they hardly ever saw each other.*

*It was* SUCH *a beautiful house* THAT *they bought it.*

*He had* SUCH *a lot of* | *work*
| *problems* | THAT *he couldn't sleep at night.*

## Exercise 1

**1 A** *The music was so wonderful that I went straight out and bought the record.*
**B** *It was such wonderful music that I went straight out and bought the record.*

Look at the example and transform the sentences from the reviews in the same way.

**2 A** ...........................................................

...........................................................

**B** ...........................................................

...........................................................

**3 A** ...........................................................

...........................................................

**B** ...........................................................

...........................................................

**4 A** ...........................................................

...........................................................

**B** ...........................................................

...........................................................

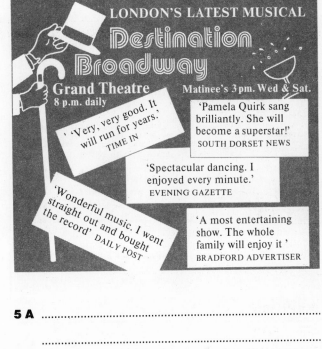

LONDON'S LATEST MUSICAL
**Destination Broadway**

**Grand Theatre** 8 p.m. daily
Matinee's 3 pm. Wed & Sat.

'Very, very good. It will run for years.' TIME IN

'Pamela Quirk sang brilliantly. She will become a superstar!' SOUTH DORSET NEWS

'Spectacular dancing. I enjoyed every minute.' EVENING GAZETTE

'Wonderful music. I went straight out and bought the record' DAILY POST

'A most entertaining show. The whole family will enjoy it' BRADFORD ADVERTISER

**5 A** ...........................................................

...........................................................

**B** ...........................................................

...........................................................

Write similar sentences about 'Sudden Departure' and 'The Wrong Connection'.

Have you read **Juliet Sotheby's** new thriller
**SUDDEN DEPARTURE**
appleseed books, £8·95

'A tense, gripping thriller. It will sell millions.' DAILY NEWS

'Absolutely fascinating. I couldn't put it down' THE LONDONER

'A winner! Terrifying. I couldn't sleep for a week' SOUTHEND STAR

'Believable story of the near future. Everyone should read it' BBC TV 'BOOKS OF THE MONTH'

'Exciting plot. It would make a marvellous film' DAILY OBSERVER

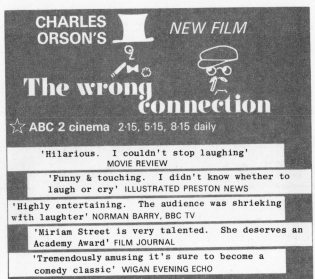

**CHARLES ORSON'S** *NEW FILM*
**The wrong connection**
☆ ABC 2 cinema 2·15, 5·15, 8·15 daily

'Hilarious. I couldn't stop laughing' MOVIE REVIEW

'Funny & touching. I didn't know whether to laugh or cry' ILLUSTRATED PRESTON NEWS

'Highly entertaining. The audience was shrieking with laughter' NORMAN BARRY, BBC TV

'Miriam Street is very talented. She deserves an Academy Award' FILM JOURNAL

'Tremendously amusing it's sure to become a comedy classic' WIGAN EVENING ECHO

## Exercise 2

Write a short review of a book, film or play.

# Unit 57

## Language summary

*There was a lounge* | *with a dance floor.*
| *which had a dance floor.*   *They heard him. He was screaming.*
*They heard him screaming.*

*many of whom/some of whom/half of whom/thirteen of whom*

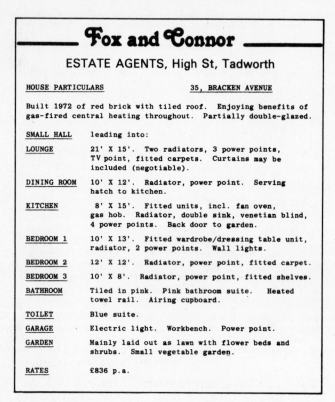

## Fox and Connor

### ESTATE AGENTS, High St, Tadworth

HOUSE PARTICULARS          35, BRACKEN AVENUE

Built 1972 of red brick with tiled roof. Enjoying benefits of gas-fired central heating throughout. Partially double-glazed.

| | |
|---|---|
| SMALL HALL | leading into: |
| LOUNGE | 21' X 15'. Two radiators, 3 power points, TV point, fitted carpets. Curtains may be included (negotiable). |
| DINING ROOM | 10' X 12'. Radiator, power point. Serving hatch to kitchen. |
| KITCHEN | 8' X 15'. Fitted units, incl. fan oven, gas hob. Radiator, double sink, venetian blind, 4 power points. Back door to garden. |
| BEDROOM 1 | 10' X 13'. Fitted wardrobe/dressing table unit, radiator, 2 power points. Wall lights. |
| BEDROOM 2 | 12' X 12'. Radiator, power point, fitted carpet. |
| BEDROOM 3 | 10' X 8'. Radiator, power point, fitted shelves. |
| BATHROOM | Tiled in pink. Pink bathroom suite. Heated towel rail. Airing cupboard. |
| TOILET | Blue suite. |
| GARAGE | Electric light. Workbench. Power point. |
| GARDEN | Mainly laid out as lawn with flower beds and shrubs. Small vegetable garden. |
| RATES | £836 p.a. |

## Exercise 1

**A** *There's a toilet which has a blue suite.*
**B** *There's a toilet with a blue suite.*

Write four more sentences of each type.

**1 A** ......................................................

...............................................................

  **B** ......................................................

**2 A** ......................................................

...............................................................

  **B** ......................................................

**3 A** ......................................................

...............................................................

  **B** ......................................................

**4 A** ......................................................

...............................................................

  **B** ......................................................

## Exercise 2

There are about fifty-five million people in the United Kingdom, of whom approximately three million are 'immigrants', that is they were born outside the United Kingdom. The immigrants, the majority of whom have arrived since 1950, have come from all over the world. Look at the chart below.

| | |
|---|---|
| 615 820 | Ireland |
| 321 995 | India |
| 171 775 | Jamaica |
| 157 680 | Germany |
| 140 000 | Pakistan/Bangladesh |
| 110 590 | USA |
| 108 980 | Italy |
| 75 295 | Cyprus |
| 64 665 | Canada |
| 59 500 | Kenya |
| 57 000 | Australia |
| 49 470 | Spain |
| 47 825 | South Africa |
| 40 500 | Uganda |
| 35 910 | France |
| 33 840 | Malta |
| 29 250 | Hong Kong |
| 28 565 | Nigeria |

**THE NEW BRITONS**
**Where do they come from ?**

(scale: 50 000, 100 000, 200 000, 300 000, 400 000, 500 000, 600 000, 650 000)

*There are 3 million immigrants, just over 40,000 of whom came from Uganda.*

Write ten sentences like this, using: more than 600,000/ about 10%/just under 1%/approximately 170,000/well over 150,000/almost 60,000/nearly 65,000/about 50,000/ approximately 75,000/around 110,000.

## Exercise 3

Max Yarmouth has a television show in Britain. He impersonates famous people. He is often asked how he manages to do it.

He videotapes them when they are performing on television. *He videotapes them performing on television.*

Continue.

**1** He listens to them as they are speaking.

...............................................................

**2** He photographs them when they are smiling and frowning.

...............................................................

**3** He imitates politicians when they are giving speeches.

...............................................................

**4** He watches singers every time they appear on TV.

...............................................................

**5** He copies them when they move their hands.

...............................................................

# Unit 58

## Language summary

*It was raining. He took his umbrella.*     *He took his umbrella BECAUSE it was raining.*

*It wasn't raining. He took his umbrella.*     ALTHOUGH
THOUGH     | *it wasn't raining, he took his umbrella.*
EVEN THOUGH

*I chose the house wine, AS this is often the best way to judge a restaurant's wine list.*

## Exercise 1

Complete the spaces with: because/although.

1 She applied for the job as personnel manager ................... she liked meeting people.

2 He got good grades in his examinations ................... he never seemed to do much work.

3 ................... he is very well-off, he drives a cheap second-hand car.

4 The workers were offered a good pay rise ................... production had increased by 20%.

5 I'm going to buy the new 'Tumbling Dice' LP ................... they're my favourite group.

6 His car refused to start ................... it had just been serviced.

## Exercise 2

He was depressed.     (He managed to smile.)     *He managed to smile although he was depressed.*
                      (He drank too much whisky.)     *He drank too much whisky because he was depressed.*

Write two sentences for each of the following.

1 She is handicapped.  (She needed a special car.)
                       (She took part in the marathon.)

2 They're very religious.  (They never go to church.)
                          (They go to church every Sunday.)

3 He fell 100 metres.  (He was killed.)
                       (He didn't hurt himself.)

4 The room was stuffy.  (She opened the window.)
                        (She didn't open the window.)

5 The programme was entertaining.  (He switched it off.)
                                   (He watched it to the end.)

6 The ring was valuable.  (She threw it into the river.)
                          (She kept it in a safe deposit box.)

7 The service had been excellent.  (They left a big tip.)
                                   (They didn't leave a tip.)

8 She was furious.  (She didn't say a word.)
                    (She shouted.)

## Exercise 3

Even though he wrote three letters, he didn't get a reply.
*He wrote three letters but he didn't get a reply.*

Rewrite these sentences in the same way.

1 They lost although they played very well.
2 Though they thought the exam had been easy, they all failed.

3 Even though she smoked, drank and never took exercise, she lived to be 100.
4 The police couldn't prove anything although they knew she was guilty.
5 He didn't get the job even though everyone thought he was the best man for it.

## Exercise 4

### GOTHAM YOUNG ASSOCIATES

*Manufacturers of quality toys since 1958*

We are looking for a young dynamic marketing executive to join our highly successful sales team in Europe. The ideal candidate will be in his or her late twenties, highly qualified with a proven track record in marketing, and will be fluent in at least one European language. Initially the successful candidate will be based in London, but will later travel extensively in Western Europe.
Excellent remuneration, company car and fringe benefits.

Further details and application form from:

Mrs D. Trim, Gotham Young Associates, North Park Industrial Estate, London NW44 3KJ.

Mrs Trim received several applications for the job. She made notes on each of the applicants. Look at the notes that she made on Colin Fisher.

| Colin Fisher (Ref OT/07) PROS | CONS |
|---|---|
| right age | – not much marketing experience |
| well-qualified | – only French, not very fluent |
| ambitious | – has never stayed long in one job |
| prepared to travel | – married with two kids |
| knows France | – little experience of rest of Europe |
| well-dressed | – bitten finger nails |
| non-smoker | – drank too much at lunch |

*Although he's the right age, he hadn't had much marketing experience.*

Write six sentences with 'although'.

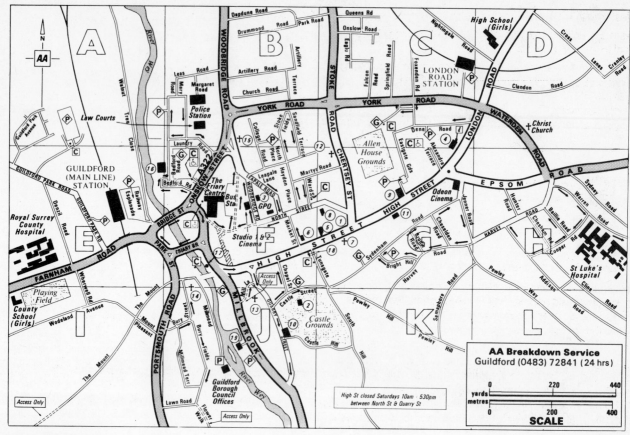

# Guildford

## CENTRAL PLAN

**C(4) Tourist Information Centre** – Civic Hall London Road *tel 67314* (see also public buildings and places of interest)

## Public buildings & places of interest

**G(1) Archbishop Abbot's (Trinity) Hospital** A picturesque brick-built building founded by George Abbot – a native of Guildford and Archbishop of Canterbury from 1611 to 1633–in 1619 as an alms-house for 12 men and 8 women

**J(2) Castle Keep and Gardens** A rectangular Norman keep of three storeys, situated in attractive gardens. Fine view from the summit.

**F(3) Citizens' Advice Bureau**

**C(4) Civic Hall and Tourist Information Centre** A modern building opened in 1962 and home of the Guildford Philharmonic Orchestra.

**G(5) Guildford House** A fine town house of 1660, noted for its beautifully-carved staircase and finely-decorated plaster ceilings. Frequently changing art exhibitions are held here.

**F(6) Guildhall** The picturesque 17th-C facade of this building which overlooks High St, is noted for its projecting clock.

**G(7) Holy Trinity Church** A late 18th-C red-bricked church standing at the top of the High Street, which contains the tomb of Archbishop Abbot.

**G(8) Library**

**G(9) Municipal Buildings**

**J(10) Museum, Castle Arch** Contains collections on local history, geology and archaeology, including those of the Surrey Archaeological Society.

**G(11) Royal Grammar School** A 16th-C building famous for its collection of chained books in the Library.

**G(12) St Joseph's Church (RC)**

**J(13) St Mary's Church** Guildford's oldest and most interesting church which preserves specimens of Saxon, Norman, Early English and Transitional architecture.

**J(14) St Nicolas' Church** Rebuilt in the late 19th C but preserving the Perpendicular Loseley Chapel, with interesting monuments of the Mores of Loseley family.

**B(15) St Saviour's Church** A late 19th C structure with a prominent tower

**E(16) Sports Centre**

**F(17) Treadwheel Crane** Restored 18th-C treadwheel crane of the old town wharf.

**G(18) Tunsgate** With its tall Tuscan columns. columns are all that remain of the old corn exchange and law courts.

**J(19) Yvonne Arnaud Theatre** Opened in 1965.

**F/G/J High Street and Quarry Street** These two streets, the former paved with granite setts, have been designated a Conservation Area. The elegant Georgian fronts of many of the buildings often hide far older backs.

## Theatres and Cinemas

**G Odeon Cinema**, Epsom Road *tel 504990*

**F Studio 1 & 2 Cinema**, Woodbridge Road *tel 64334*

**J(19) Yvonne Arnaud Theatre**, Millbrook *tel 64571* (see also public buildings and places of interest)

## Department Stores

**Debenhams Ltd**, Millbrook
**A & N Ltd**, High Street
**Marks and Spencer Ltd**, High Street
*Early closing day Wednesday*

## Markets

**F Fruit and Vegetable Market**, North Street (Friday and Saturday)

## Hospitals

**E Royal Surrey County Hospital**, Farnham Road *tel 71122*

**H St Luke's Hospital**, Warren Road *tel 504945*

## Sport and Recreation

**E(16) Sports D Centre**, Bedford Road – swimming pools etc (see also public buildings and places of interest).

## Exercise 1

Here are some of the symbols used on the map. Put the correct words next to the symbols.

| | |
|---|---|
| Car Park | One-way street |
| Post Office | Multi-storey Car Park |
| Convenience | Tourist Information Centre |
| Church | Convenience with facilities for the disabled |

1 **C** .....................................................

2 **P** .....................................................

3 **+** .....................................................

4 **→** .....................................................

5 ***i*** .....................................................

6 **C** ♿ .....................................................

7 **GPO** .....................................................

## Exercise 2

Trace the following directions on the map.

Walk out of London Road Station to York Road and turn right. Go straight along York Road for about 800 metres. Cross the major road junction with Stoke Road and continue on to the roundabout where you turn left.

Bear right at the fork and carry on to the next junction.

Bear left at the junction and then right over the bridge.

As soon as you've crossed the bridge turn sharp left and take the first street on the left. The road goes round to the right along the river bank. Follow the road to the end, walk across the car park.

Where are you? ...................................................

.......................................................................

What can you see in the middle of the river? .................

.......................................................................

What can you see on the big hill across the river? .................

.......................................................................

## Exercise 3

Write directions from the Police Station to the Castle Museum.

## Exercise 4

In Guildford, where would you go to:

1 hear a symphony concert? .........................

2 see an exhibition of paintings? .........................

3 swim indoors? .........................

4 play football? .........................

5 appear as a witness at a trial? .........................

6 see a play? .........................

7 report a stolen car? .........................

8 get a good view of Guildford? .........................

9 catch an express train? .........................

10 see a very old crane? .........................

## Exercise 5

Why wouldn't you:

1 visit Debenham's store on Wednesday afternoon? ......

.......................................................................

2 go to North Street market on Monday? .........................

.......................................................................

3 drive east along North Street? .........................

.......................................................................

4 shake hands with Archbishop Abbot? .........................

.......................................................................

5 park your car in the High Street on Saturday afternoon?

.......................................................................

6 appear as a witness at Tunsgate law courts? .........................

.......................................................................

## Exercise 6

Now write directions from your home to the school.

# Unit 60

*It was snowing so she wore a coat.*

| She wore a coat | because | it was snowing. |
|---|---|---|
| | because of | the snow. |

| Because | it was snowing | she wore a coat. |
|---|---|---|
| Because of | the snow | |

*It was snowing but she didn't wear a coat.*

| She didn't wear a coat | although | it was snowing. |
|---|---|---|
| | in spite of | the snow. |
| | despite | |

| Although | it was snowing | she didn't wear a coat. |
|---|---|---|
| In spite of | the snow | |
| Despite | | |

*It was difficult, but he managed to do it.*

| It was difficult. | However, | he managed to do it. |
|---|---|---|
| | Nevertheless, | |

| It was difficult. He managed to do it, | however. |
|---|---|
| | nevertheless. |

## Exercise

Read the following news items and fill in the spaces with: because/because of/
although/in spite of/nevertheless.

---

**IBC News**

John Curtis, the kidnapped businessman, was released today ............ no ransom had been paid. He was found in a bus shelter in the early hours of this morning with his hands and feet tied. ........... his terrible experience he was well and cheerful .......... he was tired and hungry. The police had refused to allow the family to pay the ransom, ............ they had tried on several occasions. It is thought the kidnappers released Mr Curtis after an appeal on television by his wife.

---

**IBC News**

The M1 motorway was closed for four hours today ........... a multiple crash involving hundreds of vehicles. At one point visibility was down to six metres in some places.......... thick fog, and the road surface was treacherous ........... there were patches of black ice. Motorists continued to drive too fast......... police warnings. ............ this 'motorway madness' and the terrible weather conditions, the police decided to close the motorway. The police advise motorists not to take to the roads unless their journeys are really necessary.

---

**IBC News**

An estimated 20,000 people turned out to greet the Prince of Wales in Cardiff today .......... appalling weather conditions. ................ Welsh nationalists had threatened to disrupt the visit, their shouts of protest were drowned by the cheering crowds. ........... the visit, schoolchildren had been given a holiday and the Prince's route was lined with flag-waving children. The police had mounted their tightest security operation ever. .......... the Prince managed to break free from his bodyguards and mingled with the crowd, chatting and shaking hands.

---

**IBC News**

A 14-month-old baby had a miraculous escape this afternoon. .............. a 20m fall from a 5th storey balcony, 14-month-old Steven Paine survived unhurt. Steven had somehow managed to crawl over a balcony rail. ...........he landed on concrete, he didn't even cry and was picked up by a neighbour and rushed to hospital. After an examination, Steven was able to return home with nothing worse than slight bruising.

---

**IBC News**

International Computers announced this afternoon that they have just won a £200m order .......... fierce international competition. ............. the order, placed by the government of Wibanya, the jobs of 80 employees at the Southampton factory, which had been under threat .......... falling orders, will now be saved. ............ the economic recession continues to worsen, the company is optimistic that more orders will be placed for their new NZ series of computers. ........... the company states that their Birmingham factory will still have to close with the loss of 120 jobs.

# Unit 61

## Exercise 1

Find words in the text which mean:

1 help
2 restrain by using greater strength
3 injure, using fingernails
4 took away a weapon
5 someone who looks after a building
6 much too highly priced

## Exercise 2

First they overpowered the woman. Then they charged her with armed robbery.

*After overpowering the woman, they charged her with armed robbery.*

1 First she refused to pay the fare. Then she hit the driver.

..................................................................................

..................................................................................

2 First she hit the driver. Then she fought the police who came to his aid.

..................................................................................

..................................................................................

The Times Monday 1st December 1981

# Woman of 93 hit cabbie with her walking stick

Miami, Nov 30. – A 93-year-old woman was jailed here for a night on a charge of armed robbery after she refused to pay what she considered an exorbitant taxi fare, then hit the driver with her walking stick and fought police who came to his aid.

Johanna Briscoe refused to pay the $10 (about £5) fare on Friday. When the taxi-driver protested, she hit him with her walking stick.

When the caretakers of the flats where she lives came to his aid, she attacked them too. Two policeman who came to investigate were kicked, scratched and hit with the stick.

After finally overpowering the woman, they charged her with armed robbery and resisting arrest, 'disarmed' her and took her off to prison.

Back at home, she was reported to have recovered with the aid of a large whisky and orange juice. – AFP.

3 First she got home. Then she had a large whisky.

..................................................................................

..................................................................................

Daily Mail 5th Nov. 1980

# Piranha bites a baby's hand

A FAMILY'S pet piranha fish was up for sale last night after it took a bite at their baby daughter.

The 15-inch long, flesh-eating fish named Jaws leapt clear of its tank and bit Catherine Pellegrine's finger as she trailed her hand near the water.

Her horrified mother Margaret, 36, said: 'I was shaking with fear afterwards. I just want it out of the house.'

Mrs Pellegrine's 40-year-old husband Frank, a keen tropical fish breeder, bought the fish 10 months ago for £10.50.

After the attack 17-month-old Catherine was left with a badly gashed finger. The fish simply dropped back into its tank which stands in the family's lounge at their home in Rotherham, South Yorkshire.

## Exercise 3

Read the passage and complete these sentences in your own words.

1 The fish was so dangerous that ................................................

2 It bit her finger while she was ................................................

3 Her mother was so terrified that ................................................

4 Frank's hobby is ................................................

5 The piranha's teeth were so sharp that ................................................

6 The fish was kept in ................................................

## Exercise 4

A man who is 40 years old is a 40-year-old man.

Continue.

1 A contract which is worth 15 million pounds is a ................................................

2 A suit which cost 200 dollars is ................................................

3 A journey which takes 2 hours is ................................................

4 A working week of 38 hours is ................................................

5 A lesson of 50 minutes is ................................................

6 A fish which is 15 inches long is ................................................

7 A bag of potatoes which weighs 5 kilos is ................................................

8 A tank which holds 52 litres is ................................................

# Unit 62

## Language summary

*I don't know* WHAT *to do.*
*I'll tell you* WHAT *I can.*
WHAT *I saw astonished me.*
WHAT *you need is a holiday.*

## Exercise 1

What shall I do?
*I don't know what to do.*

Rewrite these sentences in the same way.

**1** What shall I order for lunch? .........................................

..................................................................................

**2** What must I study to become a doctor? ......................

..................................................................................

**3** What should I say to the President? ...........................

..................................................................................

**4** What shall I buy my nephew for Christmas? ...............

..................................................................................

**5** What should I put at the top of the letter? ...................

..................................................................................

**6** What should I declare at customs? ............................

..................................................................................

## Exercise 2

I'll tell you everything that I can.   *I'll tell you what I can.*

Rewrite these sentences in the same way.

**1** She answered all the questions that she could.
**2** He gave them all the money that they needed.
**3** They told him everything that they knew.
**4** She packed all the things that she could.
**5** They didn't have the things that he wanted.

**6** He spent all the money that he had saved.
**7** She noted down all the information that was necessary.
**8** He translated all the words that he knew.
**9** They wrote down all the things that they could remember.
**10** He stole all the things that he needed to stay alive.

## Exercise 3

I saw something that astonished me.   *What I saw astonished me.*

Rewrite these sentences in the same way.

**1** He said something that offended a lot of people.
**2** She ate something that made her sick.
**3** He experienced something that was unforgettable.
**4** She heard something that was unbelievable.
**5** They learned something that would always be useful.

**6** They offered him something to eat that was unrecognizable.
**7** They gave him something that would help him to escape.
**8** She said something that surprised him.
**9** He saw something which looked like a flying saucer.
**10** They had to do things that seemed a waste of time.

## Exercise 4

'What' is sometimes used for emphasis.

You need a holiday.
*What you need is a holiday.*

They ought to save more money.
*What they ought to do is save more money.*

Continue.

**1** I love the way she talks. ...........................................

..................................................................................

**2** I want a nice cup of tea. ..........................................

..................................................................................

**3** We must work harder. .............................................

..................................................................................

**4** They need a warning. ..............................................

..................................................................................

**5** We should practise more. .........................................

..................................................................................

**6** She needs more exercise. .........................................

..................................................................................

# Unit 63

## Language summary

whatever, whichever, whoever, whenever, wherever, however

| | | | |
|---|---|---|---|
| *What shall I do?* | *I don't mind.* | *Do whatever you want.* | *Whatever you want.* |
| *Which shall I take?* | *It doesn't matter.* | *Take whichever you like.* | *Whichever you like.* |
| *Who shall I ask?* | *I don't know.* | *Ask whoever is there.* | *Whoever is there.* |
| *When shall I do it?* | *I don't care.* | *Do it whenever you like.* | *Whenever you like.* |
| *Where shall I go?* | *I'm not sure.* | *Go wherever you want.* | *Wherever you want.* |
| *How shall I do it?* | *It isn't important.* | *Do it however you like.* | *However you like.* |

*When the speaker is emotional (angry, surprised, etc.)* ever *can be used as a
separate word with the question words: who/what/when/where/why/how/which.*

*e.g.* *What ever are you talking about?*
*Why ever did he do that?*

## Exercise 1

Complete these 'ads' using: whatever/whichever/whoever/whenever/wherever/however.

**CLASSICAL, POP, JAZZ?**
_____ you like your music.
It will sound better on
**FONY HI-FI**

**LOCO COLA!**
YOU'LL FIND IT _____ YOU GO

_____ THE WEATHER
**Lush puppy shoes
care for your feet**

**BRITISH MOTORS CALYPSO**
Choice of 7 models. _____ you
choose there's a three year guarantee

_____ YOU'RE IN LONDON
YOU MUST VISIT US
**THE HONG KONG**
FOR THE BEST IN ORIENTAL FOOD
Regent Square Tel 01–68972

*Tinker, tailor, soldier, sailor?*
_____ YOU ARE.
THERE'S SOMETHING FOR YOU AT THE
**Earl's Court Exhibition.**

## Exercise 2

Where shall I put my coat?   *It doesn't matter. Wherever you like.*

Continue.

1 When shall I take my holiday? .....................................

2 Who shall I invite to the party? .....................................

3 How shall I cook the chicken? .....................................

4 What shall I wear for the dance? .....................................

5 Which colour shall I choose? .....................................

6 Where shall I park the car? .....................................

## Exercise 3

He said he was Julius Caesar.
*Who ever said that?*
or *Why ever did he say that?*

Respond to these statements using a question word: what/
which/who/why/how/when/where, + ever.

1 They said the world would end next Tuesday.

.....................................

2 England once beat Brazil 8–0 at football.

.....................................

3 He jumped off the Eiffel Tower and tried to fly.

.....................................

4 He painted a moustache on the Mona Lisa.

.....................................

5 They both proposed marriage to her on the same day.

.....................................

6 She broke one arm, two legs and fractured her skull.

.....................................

7 I saw a ghost once.

.....................................

8 She said I could have the Rolls, the Cadillac or the
Ferrari.

.....................................

9 She left all her money to her dog.

.....................................

# Unit 64

## Mr Jones

During the winter I lived for several months in a rooming house in Brooklyn. It was not a shabby place, but a pleasantly furnished, elderly brownstone kept hospital-neat by its owners, two maiden sisters.

Mr Jones lived in the room next to mine. My room was the smallest in the house, his the largest, a nice big sunshiny room, which was just as well, for Mr Jones never left it: all his needs, meals, shopping, laundry, were attended to by the middle-aged landladies. Also, he was not without visitors; on the average, a half-dozen various persons, men and women, young, old, in-between, visited his room each day, from early morning until late in the evening. He was not a drug dealer or a fortune-teller; no, they came just to talk to him and apparently they made him small gifts of money for his conversation and advice. If not, he had no obvious means of support.

I never had a conversation with Mr Jones myself, a circumstance I've often since regretted. He was a handsome man, about forty. Slender, black-haired, and with a distinctive face; a pale, lean face, high cheek-bones, and with a birthmark on his left cheek, a small scarlet defect shaped like a star. He wore gold-rimmed glasses with pitch-black lenses: he was blind, and crippled, too—according to the sisters, the use of his legs had been denied him by a childhood accident, and he could not move without crutches. He was always dressed in a crisply-pressed dark grey or blue three-piece suit and a subdued tie—as though about to set off for a Wall Street office.

However, as I've said, he never left the premises. Simply sat in his cheerful room in a comfortable chair and received visitors. I had no notion of why they came to see him, these rather ordinary-looking folk, or what they talked about, and I was far too concerned with my own affairs to much wonder over it. When I did, I imagined that his friends had found in him an intelligent, kindly man, a good listener in whom to confide and consult with over their troubles: a cross between a priest and a therapist.

Mr Jones had a telephone. He was the only tenant with a private line. It rang constantly, often after midnight and as early as six in the morning.

I moved to Manhattan. Several months later I returned to the house to collect a box of books I had stored there. While the landladies offered me tea and cakes in their lace-curtained 'parlour', I enquired of Mr Jones.

The women lowered their eyes. Clearing her throat, one said: 'It's in the hands of the police.'

The other offered: 'We've reported him as a missing person.'

The first added: 'Last month, twenty-six days ago, my sister carried up Mr Jones's breakfast, as usual. He wasn't there. All his belongings were there. But he was gone.'

'It's odd—'

'—how a man totally blind, a helpless cripple—'

Ten years pass.

Now it is a zero-cold December afternoon, and I am in Moscow. I am riding in a subway car. There are only a few other passengers. One of them is a man sitting opposite me, a man wearing boots, a thick long coat and a Russian-style fur cap. He has bright eyes, blue as a peacock's.

After a doubtful instant, I simply stared, for even without the black glasses, there was no mistaking that lean distinctive face, those high cheekbones with the single scarlet star-shaped birthmark.

I was just about to cross the aisle and speak to him when the train pulled into a station, and Mr Jones, on a pair of fine sturdy legs, stood up and strode out of the car. Swiftly, the train door closed behind him.

by Truman Capote in *Music for Chameleons* (1981).

## Exercise 1

Find words which mean:

1 a house where you can rent rooms
2 unable to see
3 unable to walk
4 someone who sells drugs
5 unmarried
6 bright red
7 sticks of wood or metal, used to help someone who has difficulty in walking
8 as black as tar
9 curved pieces of glass used in spectacles (glasses)
10 glasses with gold edges
11 a person who pays rent for a room or house
12 a private telephone
13 a person who treats illnesses, either physical or mental
14 softly, quietly, coloured
15 a face with little fat
16 the business centre of New York, particularly for the money market
17 slim, thin
18 dirty, in bad condition
19 building
20 someone who can tell you about the future
21 walked quickly
22 strong

## Exercise 2

Glasses with gold rims are *gold-rimmed* glasses.
A person who tells your fortune is a *fortune-teller*.

Complete the spaces below. All the words you will need are in the story.

1 A sitting-room with lace curtains is a .................... .................... room.
2 A suit with trousers, jacket and a waistcoat is a .................... .................... suit.
3 People who look ordinary are .................... .................... people.
4 A birthmark in the shape of a star is a .................... .................... birthmark.
5 A cap in a style which is worn in Russia is a .................... .................... cap.
6 A day which is very cold, with temperatures around 0°C, is a .................... .................... day.
7 A place which is as neat as a hospital is a .................... .................... place.
8 Lenses which are as black as pitch are .................... .................... lenses.
9 A landlady in her forties or fifties is a .................... .................... landlady.
10 A suit which has just been pressed and looks clean and fresh is a .................... .................... suit.
11 Instead of 'six persons', you can say 'a .................... .................... persons'.
12 You can say that someone who is neither young nor old is .................... .................... .

## Exercise 3

1 'the use of his legs had been denied him by a childhood accident' means
   ☐ A He had been told that a childhood accident was not the cause of the injury.
   ☐ B Because of a childhood accident, he couldn't walk.
   ☐ C He had been forbidden to leave the house, after running over a child.

2 'he had no obvious means of support' means
   ☐ A Not many people seemed to like him.
   ☐ B You couldn't see his crutches.
   ☐ C Nobody knew how he got enough money to live on.

3 'it's in the hands of the police' means
   ☐ A The police are investigating it.
   ☐ B The police came and took him away.
   ☐ C He's in prison.

4 'I had no notion of why they came to see him' means
   ☐ A I never saw his visitors.
   ☐ B I had no idea of the reason for their visits.
   ☐ C He never told me why they came to see him.

5 'clearing her throat' means
   ☐ A She coughed slightly.
   ☐ B She touched her throat with her hand.
   ☐ C She had a drink of water.

# Unit 65

## Exercise 1

Can you list six things which might be found in a first-aid kit?

1 ........................................................

2 ........................................................

3 ........................................................

4 ........................................................

5 ........................................................

6 ........................................................

## Exercise 2

This is a page from Dr Finlay's diary. Look at the notes on Mr Cook. Try and imagine why the other patients came to see him. Write notes about them.

### FEBRUARY 3rd, Monday      WEEK 5

9.00   *Mr Cook – backache. Has had it for 3 days. Prescribed painkiller – 2 days off work.*

9.15   *Mrs Keeping*

9.30   *Miss Harper*

9.45   *Mr Casey*

10.00   *Stephen Henchard (age 3)*

10.15   *Diane Bennett (age 1)*

10.30   *Mr Peters*

## Exercise 3

### Medical crossword

**Clues** (for answers, turn to the last page)

**Across**

1 It connects the hand to the arm. (5)
3 'You've got a ...... (4). It might be measles.'
6 She left hospital when the baby was six days ...... (3)
7 'I'm going to ...... (9) a painkiller for you.'
9 'I stood on a nail. It went into my ......' (4)
10 You ...... (5) if you get food poisoning.
12 'It's just a cold. You'd better spend a ...... (3) in bed.'
13 Another word for your backbone. (5)
14 'You fell over. Well, it's only a ...... (5). You won't need a bandage.'
15 A pain. (4)
16 'Look up. I'm going to shine this light in your ......' (4)

**Down**

1 ' ...... (8) cough' is very dangerous for young babies.
2 You take someone's temperature with this ...... (11)
4 'She was badly cut in the accident. Now her face is ......' (7)
5 Sometimes called 'German measles'. (7)
8 His temperature's high. He feels very hot and ...... (8)
11 'Open your mouth, and stick out your ......' (6)
12 'After the blow on the head, I felt ......' (5)

# Unit 66

## The Martians Are Coming

At eight o'clock on the evening of Sunday, October 30th 1938 thousands of Americans tuned in to CBS radio for 'The Mercury Theatre of the Air.' Just after the programme began it was interrupted by what sounded like the weather forecast. A minute or so later it was replaced by a programme of dance music. Suddenly a solemn voice came over the air to warn Americans, 'Ladies and gentlemen. I have a grave announcement to make ...'

The speaker then went on to describe how strange beings from the planet Mars had landed in North America. They were using poisonous gas and death-ray machines to sweep all resistance before them in a series of bloody battles. The USA was being taken over by creatures from outer space!

The broadcast continued with a confusing series of announcements, often broken by long, chilling silences. The voice of the President was heard appealing to people not to panic. An announcer on the top of the CBS skyscraper in New York described how Manhattan was being overrun. His commentary broke off in a horrible, strangled scream.

That was the end of the programme. Its producer, Orson Welles, and the cast of actors left the studio. They had completed their radio play, which had been based on 'War of the Worlds,' a science-fiction novel by H G Wells. They didn't realize what effect their play had had. Thousands of people had fled from their homes. The roads were jammed with cars racing for the hills. Some of the cars were piled high with furniture. State reserve troopers rushed to volunteer to defend the world. Sailors in the US Navy were recalled to their ships in New York harbour. Switchboards were completely jammed with people trying to call relatives and friends. In the South, people were praying in the streets. Some people even claimed that they had seen the Martians. The next morning's newspapers revealed that it had only been a radio play. It had all been a terrible mistake.

### Exercise 1

Find words or phrases which mean:

1 to adjust the controls of a radio or TV to a particular station
2 two words, both of which mean 'serious'
3 machines designed to kill people by using radiation
4 a programme sent out by radio or TV
5 a period without sound, which makes you feel cold with fear
6 a very tall building
7 a noise someone might make when their throat was being squeezed
8 the group of people acting in a play or film
9 tightly filled with ...
10 many things placed on top of each other
11 a soldier
12 a panel used for making connections by telephone

### Exercise 2

Complete this table.

| | | |
|---|---|---|
| *flee* | *fled* | *fled* |
| .................. | .................. | begun |
| .................. | swept | .................. |
| .................. | overran | .................. |
| oversimplify | .................. | .................. |
| undertake | .................. | .................. |

| | | |
|---|---|---|
| .................. | .................. | underwritten |
| .................. | .................. | fed |
| .................. | meant | .................. |
| underdo | .................. | .................. |
| override | .................. | .................. |
| overfly | .................. | .................. |

### Exercise 3

Write full answers to these questions.

1 What was the name of the programme?
2 Who was it produced by?
3 Which novel was it based on?
4 Who was the novel written by?
5 What kind of novel was it?
6 Was the programme really interrupted by the weather forecast?
7 Do you think it was really the President's voice?
8 Where was the announcer?
9 What might listeners have thought had happened to him?
10 What did state reserve troopers do?
11 What happened to the switchboards?
12 Had any people actually seen Martians?

# Unit 67

## Exercise 1

**A** Let's go out tonight.

(B doesn't want to, so he says he'd rather do something else.)

**B** *I'd rather we didn't. I'd rather we* | *watched television.*
                                              | *stayed in.*
                                              | *went to bed early.*

Continue.

**1 A** Let's go for a walk.

**B** ......................................................................................................

**2 A** Why don't we have a Chinese meal tonight?

**B** ......................................................................................................

**3 A** We've won £5,000. We can buy a new car!

**B** ......................................................................................................

**4 A** Shall we go to France for our holiday?

**B** ......................................................................................................

## Exercise 2

I'm not a child, you know.
*It isn't as if I were a child, you know.*
Continue.

**1** I didn't do it deliberately. ...............................................

**2** I'm not stupid, you know. ...............................................

**3** I'm not a millionaire, you know. ...............................................

**4** I don't come late every day! ...............................................

## Exercise 3

Read all the sentences carefully. Read all the responses below.
Put the letter for the most appropriate response in the spaces provided.

**1** Shall we run? ........
**2** I make it 9.38. ........
**3** Bye! ........
**4** Can you take a message? ........
**5** Shall we stop for coffee? ........
**6** Are you ready yet? ........
**7** You're late. ........
**8** Mark's just arrived. ........
**9** Do the washing up. ........
**10** Did you miss the beginning? ........
**11** Is it time to go? ........
**12** When will you have the money? ........
**13** He's playing the trombone. ........
**14** What time's dinner? ........
**15** What's the delay? ........

**A** Oh, not for an hour at least.
**B** Yes, it's about time we left.
**C** No, I'm afraid we haven't got time.
**D** I make it 9.40.
**E** Oh, no, not at this time of night.
**F** Hold on, I'll just get a pencil.
**G** About time too!
**H** No, there's no need to hurry.
**I** See you later.
**J** I was just about to do it, dear.
**K** Almost, I won't be long.
**L** No, we were just in time.
**M** Yes, we had a long wait at the station.
**N** Well, it'll take me a long time to save it.
**O** It always takes ages during the rush hour.

# Unit 68

## Exercise 1

Read the text and the questionnaire. Ask another student the questions, and complete the questionnaire.

## Exercise 2

Read the text again. Imagine you have just walked past a neighbour's house. You know your neighbour is on holiday. There's a ladder against the wall, and an upstairs window is open. As you came along the street, you saw a man and a woman get into a van outside the house, and drive away. You have just phoned the police. Look at the instructions, and report the incident to them.

.............................................................................
.............................................................................
.............................................................................
.............................................................................
.............................................................................
.............................................................................
.............................................................................
.............................................................................
.............................................................................
.............................................................................

# Unit 69

**Language summary**

| It/They | is/are<br>was/were<br>has/have been<br>is/are being<br>will be<br>can be<br>may be<br>has/have to be | done. |
|---|---|---|

## Exercise 1

Complete the spaces in this text.

Thousands of objects are left ................... London Transport vehicles every year. ................... of them are handed in ................... are kept at London Transport ................... Property Office. Some of the ................... items are claimed and those ................... are not are auctioned. Umbrellas, ................... and toys are the most ................... items, but some very strange ................... have been found. A stuffed life-size gorilla ................... left sitting in an underground ................... . An invalid's chair was left ................... a bus. Human bones, which ................... wrapped in brown paper, were ................... in to an astonished bus ................... . Spectacles and false teeth are ................... found and this can create ................... problem when the owner comes ................... collect them. One man arrived ................... claim a top set of ................... teeth. Hundreds of sets were ................... before he found the set ................... matched his bottom set.

## Exercise 2

The Prime Minister spoke on television last night. These are some of the things that were said. Transform them into the passive.

You elected us two years ago.
*We were elected two years ago.*

**1** We have achieved many things since then. ................

.................................................................

**2** We reduced personal taxes a year ago. .....................

.................................................................

**3** We are conquering inflation. ...............................

.................................................................

**4** However, we can't do everything at once. ...................

.................................................................

**5** We have to make some difficult choices. ....................

.................................................................

**6** We hold regular meetings with employers and trades unions. ...............................................

.................................................................

**7** We will increase pensions next year. ......................

.................................................................

**8** We may achieve a 3% growth rate next year. ...........

.................................................................

## Exercise 3

When the people of London wake up, they find letters behind the door, milk on the doorstep and the rubbish bins empty. When they go to work the streets are clean, newspapers are on the stands and there is fresh fruit and vegetables in the shops. All these things are done during the night.

*Letters have been delivered.*

Write five more sentences.

**1** ................................................................

**2** ................................................................

**3** ................................................................

**4** ................................................................

**5** ................................................................

# Unit 70

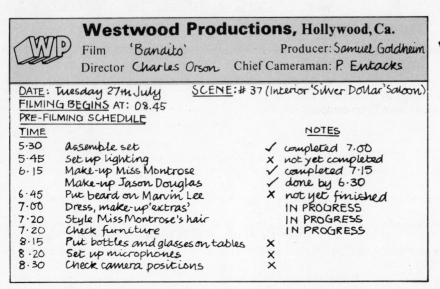

**Westwood Productions,** Hollywood, Ca.

Film  'Bandito'  Producer: Samuel Goldheim

Director  Charles Orson  Chief Cameraman: P. Entacks

DATE: Tuesday 27th July  SCENE: # 37 (Interior 'Silver Dollar' Saloon)

FILMING BEGINS AT: 08.45

PRE-FILMING SCHEDULE

| TIME | | NOTES |
|---|---|---|
| 5.30 | Assemble set | ✓ completed 7.00 |
| 5.45 | Set up lighting | ✗ not yet completed |
| 6.15 | Make-up Miss Montrose | ✓ completed 7.15 |
| | Make-up Jason Douglas | ✓ done by 6.30 |
| 6.45 | Put beard on Marvin Lee | ✗ not yet finished |
| 7.00 | Dress, make-up 'extras' | IN PROGRESS |
| 7.20 | Style Miss Montrose's hair | IN PROGRESS |
| 7.20 | Check furniture | IN PROGRESS |
| 8.15 | Put bottles and glasses on tables | ✗ |
| 8.20 | Set up microphones | ✗ |
| 8.30 | Check camera positions | ✗ |

## Exercise 1

It's 7.30. Charles Orson has just arrived on the set of 'Bandito', his new western. The assistant director has just shown him the check-list above, and is explaining it to him.

**Orson**  *Has Miss Montrose's hair been styled yet?*
**Assistant**  *I'm afraid not. It's being done at the moment.*

Write ten more exchanges like this.

## Exercise 2

Later that day, Charles Orson went to the producer to complain about the morning's arrangements.
*'When I got there, Miss Montrose was still being made up. The camera positions hadn't been checked.'*

Write six more sentences.

**1** ...........................................................................................................................

...........................................................................................................................

**2** ...........................................................................................................................

...........................................................................................................................

**3** ...........................................................................................................................

...........................................................................................................................

**4** ...........................................................................................................................

...........................................................................................................................

**5** ...........................................................................................................................

...........................................................................................................................

**6** ...........................................................................................................................

...........................................................................................................................

The producer said, *'Well, what had been done?'*
Write three sentences.  **8** ....................................................................

**7** ..........................................................  **9** ....................................................................

# Unit 71

## Language summary

*(There's a lot) to be (done).*

| *(It) will have to be done* | *by September.* |
| | *in two years time.* |
| | *before the end of the year.* |

The Republic of Wibanya is building a new capital, Wibanya City. It's being built on the banks of the River Banya . It was started five years ago, and three projects have already been finished. The government hope that it will be finished in about ten years time. They hope to move to Wibanya City in about five years time, although many buildings won't have been completed by that time. There will still be a lot to be done.

```
WIBANYA CITY - BUILDING SCHEDULE

Highway one - completed 3 yrs. ago
Banya Bridge -     "    "   "    "
Highway two - finished before rainy season
                              this year
Airport - one runway open. Completion 3 yrs.
Parliament Building - Foundations laid last yr.
                         Completion 2 yrs.
National Library - commences next yr.
                    Compl. 4 yrs.
University - Building underway. Opens
                5 yrs time
National Hospital - Compl. next month.
Bus Terminal - bldg. comm. last yr.
                    Finished in Sept.
M. of Education - compl. 4 yrs.
M. of Interior - compl. 7 mnths.
M. of Foreign Affairs - begins next week.
                         Fin. 18 months.
President's Palace - building comm.
                next year. Completion ??
Kawee Bridge - completion Jan. next yr.
Winkee Bridge - opens next month.
```

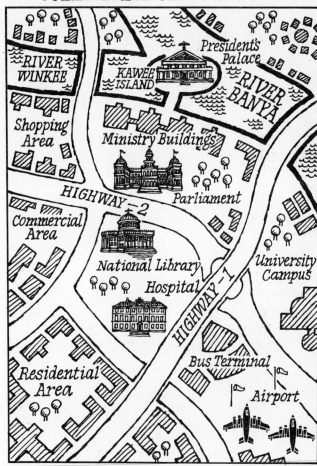

**✳ WIBANYA CITY PLAN ✳**

## Exercise 1

Answer these questions in full.

1 Where is the capital being built?
2 When was it started?
3 How many projects have been finished?
4 When will it all be finished?
5 When will the government move there?
6 Will everything have been completed?
7 How much will there be to be done?

## Exercise 2

Highway 1    *Highway 1 was completed three years ago.*

Write sentences in the past about:

1 The Banya Bridge    ..............................................

..........................................................................

2 The Parliament Building    ...............................

..........................................................................

3 The bus terminal    ...........................................

..........................................................................

## Exercise 3

Write six sentences using 'to be (done)'.

## Exercise 4

*The Ministry of Education will have been completed in four years time.*

Write sentences using 'will have been (done)', about:

1 Highway 2                 6 The Kawee Bridge
2 The airport               7 The Winkee Bridge
3 The National Hospital     8 The National Library
4 The bus terminal          9 The Ministry of the Interior
5 The Foreign Ministry      10 The President's Palace

# Unit 72

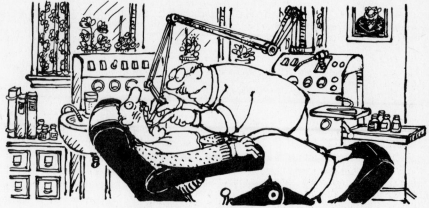

## Exercise 1

Look at the words in the box. Read them all carefully. Make ten sentences like this.

*(His) tooth needed filling, so (he) went to the dentist's to get it filled.*

| | | |
|---|---|---|
| embassy | *tooth* | service |
| garage | watch | renew |
| travel agent's | passport | type |
| clinic | hair | wash |
| laundry | baggage | *fill* |
| jeweller's | signature | change |
| secretarial | shirts | repair |
|   agency | flight | clear |
| *dentist's* | bandage | witness |
| customs | manuscript | cut |
| hairdresser's | car | confirm |
| lawyer | | |

1 .......................................................................

.......................................................................

2 .......................................................................

.......................................................................

3 .......................................................................

4 .......................................................................

5 .......................................................................

6 .......................................................................

7 .......................................................................

8 .......................................................................

9 .......................................................................

10 .......................................................................

## Exercise 2

Look at the words in the box. Make eight sentences like this.

*(She's) going to the dry cleaner's to have (her) cardigan cleaned.*

| | | |
|---|---|---|
| teacher | *cardigan* | take |
| photographer's | suit | make |
| optician's | house | X-ray |
| clinic | portrait | photo-copy |
| *dry cleaner's* | chest | correct |
| an architect | homework | test |
| copy-shop | eyes | design |
| an artist | documents | *clean* |
| tailor's | photo | paint |

1 .......................................................................

.......................................................................

2 .......................................................................

.......................................................................

3 .......................................................................

4 .......................................................................

5 .......................................................................

6 .......................................................................

7 .......................................................................

8 .......................................................................

# Unit 73

## Bermuda

Bermuda lies in the Western Atlantic Ocean some 600 miles east of North Carolina and 3000 miles west of Europe. It consists of a group of approximately 150 closely-knit islands of which the seven largest are linked together by bridges and causeways forming 'Mainland' Bermuda, roughly 22 miles long, with an average width of half to one mile. On the map, Bermuda resembles a scorpion or a fish hook.

Bermuda is the summit of a sub-marine volcano which exploded into life some 100 million years ago. Coral reefs almost entirely surround the islands, proving treacherous to shipping during the last three hundred years, but creating beautifully calm inshore waters for bathers, snorkellers and scuba divers as well as a paradise for fishing enthusiasts.

There are no freshwater streams in Bermuda so that Bermudians are forced to rely on rainwater or, in times of drought, imported water. Every house on the island has a white lime-washed roof on which the rain is caught and channelled into a tank. The government and some of the larger hotels operate desalination plants.

In the late 19th century the tourist trade came to Bermuda – since when it has grown increasingly profitable and today tourism is the island's single most important revenue earner.

Bermuda is the oldest self-governing colony of Britain with the third oldest parliament in the world.

### GENERAL INFORMATION

☐ Entry Requirements *Passports and visas* As these requirements are subject to change, please consult your British Airways office or travel agent. *Health* A vaccination certificate against smallpox is required for visitors arriving from an infected area; vaccination against typhoid and polio recommended. (Current requirements should be checked when buying your ticket.)

☐ Drugs and Firearms The importation of illegal drugs (including marijuana) and firearms is strictly prohibited and persons convicted of these offences are liable to heavy fines and/or imprisonment.

☐ Currency 100 cents = 1 Bermudian dollar. *Notes* 1, 5, 10, 20 and 50 dollars. *Coins* 1, 5, 10, 25 and 50 cents. The Bermudian dollar is on a par with the US dollar. US and Canadian currency are readily accepted (Canadian currency is liable to a discount), as are US and Canadian travellers cheques. Credit cards are accepted by a number of hotels and in most shops and restaurants.

☐ Electric Current 110 volts 60 cycle AC.

☐ Tipping The following are customary rates. *Airport:* porters 25c per suitcase. *Hotel:* 10% or $4.50 per person per day is added to your bill. *Restaurants and nightclubs:* 15% of bill. *Hairdresser:* 10–15% of bill. *Bars:* Barmen 15% of bill. *Taxi-drivers,* etc: 10–15% of bill (for full-day tour a minimum of $2.00). *Note* There is an airport departure tax of $5.00.

☐ National Holidays New Year's Day, Good Friday, Bermuda Day (May); The Queen's Birthday (June), Annual Cup Match (2 days in July), Remembrance Day (November), Christmas Day, Boxing Day.

☐ Climate: average temperatures

|  | winter | | | | | summer | | | | | | |
|---|---|---|---|---|---|---|---|---|---|---|---|---|
|  | Nov. | Dec. | Jan. | Feb. | Mar. | Apr. | May | Jun. | Jul. | Aug. | Sep. | Oct. |
|  | F C | F C | F C | F C | F C | F C | F C | F C | F C | F C | F C | F C |
| Max. | 74 23 | 70 21 | 68 20 | 67 19 | 68 20 | 70 21 | 75 24 | 79 26 | 84 29 | 86 30 | 84 30 | 80 27 |
| Min. | 64 18 | 60 16 | 60 16 | 56 14 | 59 15 | 62 17 | 67 19 | 72 22 | 76 24 | 77 25 | 75 24 | 71 22 |
| Humidity | 74% | 76% | 75% | 73% | 71% | 73% | 77% | 81% | 79% | 78% | 77% | 77% |
| Rainfall (in.) | 6.4 | 5.1 | 5.3 | 4.1 | 4.0 | 3.9 | 3.6 | 6.0 | 4.2 | 5.3 | 5.6 | 6.1 |

☐ Handicapped Visitors. For information about the appropriate hotels and the many facilities for handicapped visitors to Bermuda, write to the Society for Advancement of Travel for the Handicapped, PO Box 449, Hamilton 5.

[© British Airways, 1980]

## Exercise 1

Read the text and answer these questions.

1 What is the chief industry? .........................................

2 How far is it from Europe? .........................................

3 How many islands are there? .........................................

4 How long is the 'mainland'? .........................................

5 Which vaccination must you have had? .....................

6 Which ones should you have had? .............................

7 How many Bermudian dollars are equal to US $5?

.................................................................................

8 If you spent $20 in a restaurant, what tip would you

leave? ...................................................................

9 Which are the hottest months? .................................

.................................................................................

10 Which is the coldest month? .....................................

11 Which is the wettest month? .....................................

12 Which is the driest month? .........................................

13 How many countries have parliaments older than

Bermuda? ...............................................................

14 Why do Bermudians have to rely on rainwater? ........

.................................................................................

15 Why has Bermuda always been dangerous for shipping?

.................................................................................

16 Would electrical appliances from your country work in

Bermuda? ...............................................................

17 Does your country have more or fewer national

holidays? ................................................................

18 Which town would disabled people write to for

information? ............................................................

## Exercise 2

Read the text, and describe your country in a similar way. (About 300 words.)

# Unit 74

## Language summary

| ask, remind invite, advise, promise, offer, refuse, warn, instruct, order, force, beg, threaten, | (someone) | to do (something). not to do (something). |
|---|---|---|

## Exercise 1

'If I were you, I'd go to the dentist.'
*He/She advised me/him/her to go to the dentist.*

Look at the Language summary. Use each of the reporting verbs once only.

**1** 'If I were you, I wouldn't carry so much money.'

......................................................................

......................................................................

**2** 'I'll definitely pay you back on Friday.'

......................................................................

......................................................................

**3** 'Change gear, signal and turn right.'

......................................................................

......................................................................

**4** 'Would you wait outside for a few minutes?'

......................................................................

......................................................................

**5** 'Don't forget to turn off the lights and lock the door.'

......................................................................

......................................................................

**6** 'If you don't leave immediately I'll call the police.'

......................................................................

......................................................................

**7** 'You'd better not park here. It's dangerous.'

......................................................................

......................................................................

**8** 'No, I won't do the washing up. It's your turn.'

......................................................................

......................................................................

**9** 'Would you like to join us for coffee?'

......................................................................

......................................................................

**10** 'Oh please, don't leave me! I need you!'

......................................................................

......................................................................

**11** 'Show me your driving licence. I'm a police officer.'

......................................................................

......................................................................

**12** 'This is a gun. Give me the money, slowly. That's right.'

......................................................................

......................................................................

**13** 'Shall I put that case on the rack for you?'

......................................................................

......................................................................

## Exercise 2

He reminded her to go to the post office.
*'Don't forget to go to the post office.'*

**1** She reminded him to set the alarm.

......................................................................

......................................................................

**2** He refused to lend him any more money.

......................................................................

......................................................................

**3** They begged her to help them.

......................................................................

......................................................................

**4** She invited him to visit the school.

......................................................................

......................................................................

**5** He instructed her to switch on and press the record button.

......................................................................

**6** She promised to send them a postcard.

......................................................................

......................................................................

**7** He warned them not to eat it because it was poisonous.

......................................................................

......................................................................

**8** He ordered the soldier to salute when he met an officer.

......................................................................

......................................................................

**9** They asked her to explain it again.

......................................................................

......................................................................

**10** They forced him to open the safe.

......................................................................

......................................................................

# Unit 75

## Language summary

Reporting statements.

## Exercise 1

*Mr and Mrs N. said that they had enjoyed themselves enormously.*

Continue.

1 ................................................................................................................
2 ................................................................................................................
3 ................................................................................................................
4 ................................................................................................................
5 ................................................................................................................
6 ................................................................................................................
7 ................................................................................................................
8 ................................................................................................................
9 ................................................................................................................

## Exercise 2

### Continental Computers Ltd.
#### 1982   Chairman's Report

'I am pleased to announce that 1982 has been a very good year for the company in spite of the world recession. Overall sales have increased 20% and most of the increase has been in exports. There is great demand for our TX range of computers and we will be developing a larger version next year. Our two main factories are working at full capacity and our Manchester factory is being enlarged.

We are fairly optimistic about the future although much will depend on the value of sterling and world trading conditions. We have repaid most of the money borrowed from the banks last year. However, we are still able to announce increased profits and an increased dividend of 12p per share. We are also offering one free share for every four held.'

|                   | 1981    | 1982   |
|-------------------|---------|--------|
| Sales             | £319.8m | £383m  |
| Trading Profit    | £30.1m  | £34.2m |
| Profit before tax | £26.1m  | £28.6m |
| Earnings per share| 13.4p   | 17.2p  |
| Dividend          | 10.0p   | 12p    |

Report the Chairman's statement, beginning:

*The Chairman said that he was pleased ...*

# Unit 76

**Language summary**

Reporting questions
'What time is it?'     *(He) asked (me) what time it was.*
'Did you enjoy yourself.     (She) asked (me) if I had enjoyed (myself).*

## Exercise

When Roy Porter arrived at Heathrow Airport, he was stopped by a market researcher who asked him some questions. Look at the completed form, and report the questions and answers.

**1** What's your name?
   **A** *She asked him what his name was.*
   **B** *He said it was Roy Porter.*

**2** Are you British?
   **A** .......................................................................
   ........................................................................
   **B** .......................................................................
   ........................................................................

**3** How old are you?
   **A** .......................................................................
   ........................................................................
   **B** .......................................................................
   ........................................................................

**4** Which airport did you fly from?
   **A** .......................................................................
   ........................................................................
   **B** .......................................................................
   ........................................................................

**5** Did you fly British Airways?
   **A** .......................................................................
   ........................................................................
   **B** .......................................................................

**6** Can you tell me the flight number?
   **A** .......................................................................
   **B** .......................................................................

**7** Did you travel first class?
   **A** .......................................................................
   **B** .......................................................................

**8** Have you been on holiday or business?
   **A** .......................................................................
   **B** .......................................................................

**9** How long will you be in the UK ?
   **A** .......................................................................
   **B** .......................................................................

**10** Will you be staying in a hotel?
   **A** .......................................................................
   **B** .......................................................................

**11** How will you get home?
   **A** .......................................................................
   **B** .......................................................................

---

**MARKET RESEARCH**    **Heathrow Airport: Passenger Survey**

**1. NAME:** Roy Porter     **2. NATIONALITY:** British

**3. AGE:** 38     **4. AIRPORT OF DEPARTURE:** Brussels

**5. AIRLINE:** British Airways    **6. FLIGHT No:** BA 387

**7. FARE BASIS:**    1st class ☐    Full fare ☑    Tourist ☐
        Charter ☐    Standby ☐

**8. PURPOSE OF TRAVEL:**    Holiday ☐    Business ☑
   Family reasons ☐   Educational ☐   Immigration ☐   Other ☐

**9. LENGTH OF STAY IN U.K.:**
   Returning home ☑    Overnight ☐    Less than one week ☐
   Less than one month ☐    More than one month ☐

**10. WHERE WILL YOU BE STAYING:**
   Home ☑      Hotel ☐     Self-catering ☐
   Camping ☐    With friends ☐    Private family ☐

**11. MEANS OF TRANSPORT:**   Airport bus ☐   Underground ☐
   Coach ☐    Hire car ☐    Taxi ☐    Private car ☑

# Unit 77

## Language summary

Reporting conversations.
*The use of reporting verbs other than 'say', 'ask', and 'tell'.*

## Exercise 1

She invited him to a party.
*Would you like to come to a party next weekend?*
or *We're having a party tomorrow. Can you come?*
or *I hope you'll be able to come to my party on Friday.*

Write sentences like these for the following:

**1** He agreed to sign the contract.
**2** She greeted them formally.
**3** She arranged to meet her at midnight.
**4** He complimented her on her cooking.
**5** The motorist wanted the tank filled and the oil checked.

**6** She thanked them warmly for their presents.
**7** He admitted that he hadn't been telling the truth.
**8** The prisoner refused to answer any more questions.
**9** She offered to drive him to the station.
**10** He explained that he had lost his way.

## Exercise 2

Report these sentences. Use each of the verbs in the box below once.

| | | |
|---|---|---|
| remember | deny | admit |
| apologize | invite | add |
| suggest | beg | exclaim |
| hear | | |

**1** Would you like to go for a walk?
**2** We could go to that new Italian restaurant.
**3** Oh, my God! It's you!
**4** Oh yes, the little hotel overlooking the bay.
**5** And another thing. I think you're selfish.
**6** Please, please. Don't switch the light off.
**7** I'm terribly sorry I'm late.
**8** I really didn't do anything wrong.
**9** There will be an election next month. It was on the radio.
**10** All right. It was me. I did it.

## Exercise 3

This is an extract from page 122 of 'Trust the heart'. Complete the spaces using one each of these verbs.

| | | |
|---|---|---|
| enquired | promised | whispered |
| shouted | said | replied |
| sighed | exclaimed | murmured |
| interrupted | | |

Damian stood in the chill morning air, gazing at the dirty glass roof of the railway station. Where was Melinda? She had ......................... to say 'goodbye'. The train was due in a few moments. Then he saw her, the morning sunlight dancing in her hair.

'Damian!' she ........................ , 'Damian!'

'Melinda . . .!' he ........................ softly, 'I thought that . . .

She ........................ him. 'You thought I wouldn't come. I know that.'

'Oh, no. I was just afraid that . . .' His voice shook with emotion.

'I had to come', she ........................ 'In spite of everything, I had to.'

'I'm so glad. But is this goodbye forever?' he ........................

'You know what my father said', she ........................

'So, it is goodbye, then', he ........................ firmly.

'No, Damian . . . no', she ........................ 'I've brought my suitcase. We can get married in London, that is, if you'll have me.'

'Melinda! My darling!' he ........................ 'Why, this is the most wonderful ...

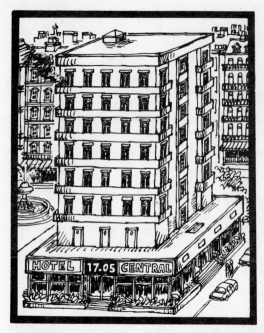

## Picture 1

How do you think the fire might have started?

Suggest six possibilities.

1 ....................................................................................................

2 ....................................................................................................

3 ....................................................................................................

4 ....................................................................................................

5 ....................................................................................................

6 ....................................................................................................

## Picture 2

Imagine the conversation between the man and the woman.
(You may make the conversation longer if you wish.)

**Man** .............................................................................................

**Woman** .........................................................................................

**Man** .............................................................................................

**Woman** .........................................................................................

**Man** .............................................................................................

**Woman** .........................................................................................

## Picture 3

Write the conversation between the man, the operator and the fire service.
(You may make the conversation longer if you wish.)

**Operator** .......................................................................................

**Man** .............................................................................................

**Operator** .......................................................................................

**Fire Service** ..................................................................................

**Man** .............................................................................................

**Fire Service** ..................................................................................

**Man** .............................................................................................

**Fire Service** ..................................................................................

**Man** .............................................................................................

**Fire Service** ..................................................................................

## Picture 4

Describe what's happening in the picture.

## Picture 5

There were 250 people in the hotel. Only a few died. Say how you think the
others escaped, and how they managed to do it. Say how the victims of the
fire died. Complete the story.

# Unit 79

## BRITISH AND AMERICAN ENGLISH

It has been said that the British and Americans are 'two peoples *separated* by a common language.' However the differences between British and American English are comparatively small. Although British newspapers occasionally publish letters from irate elderly citizens complaining that they are unable to understand a word of the latest American TV series, it is clear that few people have serious problems. In fact people on both sides of the Atlantic might have much more difficulty in understanding the stronger regional dialects of their own country than in understanding an average speaker from the other country. Television, films, and pop music have helped to bridge the Atlantic and those minor difficulties which might occur in comprehension are probably much fewer than 40 or 50 years ago. It is quite normal to find four or five American programmes in an evening on British television, and to find that 6 or 7 of the American Top 20 LP records are by British artists. It is true that most Americans would say:

'Pardon me, Do you have .....?'
while in Britain it would be more common to say:
'Excuse me, Have you got .....?'
However both forms would be understood in both countries. One of the most obvious areas of difference would relate to words connected with motoring, for example:

| British | American |
|---|---|
| motor car | automobile |
| saloon | sedan |
| bumper | fender |
| bonnet | hood |
| boot | trunk |
| estate car | station wagon |
| petrol | gas (or gasoline) |
| accelerator | gas pedal |
| gear change | gear shift |
| silencer | muffler |

This is probably because cars were developed separately in each country in the early years of this century, before Hollywood exposed the British to American culture! Of course, an American who asked for 'gas' in a British 'filling station' would get what he wanted, and in the same way an Englishman who asked for 'petrol' in a 'gas station' would drive away with a full tank. The British talk about 'postmen', but the 'post' is carried in 'mail bags', on 'mail vans', to 'mail trains'. The Americans usually say 'mail men', but still talk about 'postage stamps', 'postcards' and 'post offices'.

### Exercise 1

Read the text, and put these words in the correct columns below:

gas/mailman/hood/gear shift/boot/filling station/petrol/postman/accelerator/sedan/station wagon/gas station.

| British | American |
|---|---|
| ................. | ................. |
| ................. | ................. |
| ................. | ................. |
| ................. | ................. |
| ................. | ................. |
| ................. | ................. |

### Exercise 2

Here are some pairs of words. One of each pair is more common in British English, the other in American English. Try and find out which one is British, and which is American. Put them in the correct columns:

| | |
|---|---|
| curtains/drapes | faucet/tap |
| depot/station | autumn/fall |
| movies/films | conductor/guard |
| pharmacy/chemist's | ill/sick |
| lift/elevator | mad/angry |
| pavement/sidewalk | center/centre |
| apartment/flat | theatre/theater |
| motorway/highway | high school/secondary school |

| British | American |
|---|---|
| ................. | ................. |
| ................. | ................. |
| ................. | ................. |
| ................. | ................. |
| ................. | ................. |
| ................. | ................. |
| ................. | ................. |
| ................. | ................. |

### Exercise 3

Look at the following examples of American English and rewrite them in British English.

1 Did you take your vacation yet? ..................................
..................................

2 Do you have a pen? ..................................
..................................

3 He could have gotten killed. ..................................
..................................

4 He visited with his friends. ..................................
..................................

5 I saw him Friday. ..................................
..................................

6 I stayed home last night. ..................................
..................................

7 It's a quarter after six. ..................................
..................................

# Unit 80

## Exercise 1

Read Unit 80 in the Student's Book. Write a postcard from Gina to Mr Jenkins at the Hamlet School of English, Durham House, St Wilfred's Road, Bournemouth, BH38 7DU, England. Thank him and all the other teachers for all the help they gave you. Say that with your improved English you will be able to get a good job. Promise to call in and see them when you are in England next year.

## Exercise 2

Write a postcard from Gina to Jacques. Tell him where you are and tell him that you've got a job. Inquire about the other students in the class. Ask him if he passed his exam and invite him to visit you if ever he's in Rome. Remind him that he's got your address and phone number.

## Exercise 3

Write a letter from Gina to her hostess, Mrs Sharples. Tell her that you had a pleasant flight and arrived safely. Apologize for not phoning. Thank her for everything she did and enquire about Mr Sharples and 'Woodhouse', the dog. Send your regards to one or two other people. Promise to visit them next summer when you will be in England on holiday. Invite them to come and visit you in Rome. Assure them that they would be welcome. Promise to show them all the sights and say that you'll cook them a real Italian dinner. Say that you very much hope they'll be able to come.

# Revision

Read through Units 41–80 in the Student's book, and answer these questions.

**Unit**

41  Complete this saying: 'An apple a day...' ......................................................................................

42  What does Shirley wish she hadn't done? ......................................................................................

43  What doesn't Joyce regret doing? ......................................................................................

44  What does Grace Field do? ......................................................................................

45  Who was 003? ......................................................................................

46  Where did 006 go after Washington and what did he do there? ..............................................

47  What is a widow? ......................................................................................

48  Who was killed by a falling chimney? ......................................................................................

49  Why is Barry Foot most shocked? ......................................................................................

50  Who is Paola Rossi? ......................................................................................

51  Describe the room you are in at the moment. ......................................................................................

52  Briefly describe the girl with the handbag. ......................................................................................

53  Why did the Chancellor propose to reduce income tax? ........................................................

54  Why is Mr Miller going to design a 'bleeper'? ......................................................................................

55  Why should you keep plastic bags away from babies? ........................................................

56  Why was it easy for Luke to start conversations? ....................................................................

57  Why was the smoking room pressurized? ......................................................................................

58  Why did Rebecca Mitchell have a milk shake even though she didn't like milk shakes? ............

59  Give directions from Oxford Circus to Westminster by tube. ....................................................

60  Why was the football match stopped twice? ......................................................................................

61  What is the Open University? ......................................................................................

62  What was Philip asking Melanie? ......................................................................................

63  Where can Alan leave his motorbike? ......................................................................................

64  Where would you go if you wanted to change the shape of your nose? ..................................

65  Why isn't Mrs Mallard happy with her pills? ......................................................................................

66  What did Voyager I discover about Saturn? ......................................................................................

67  What would Pam rather do in the morning? ......................................................................................

68  Write down three other words which all mean 'policeman'. ....................................................

69  How are gold flakes used in traditional Indian cooking? ........................................................

70  What is happening outside Dawson City? ......................................................................................

71  What will the Wessex Water Authority have done before the circus arrives? ........................

72  Why won't Adrian be able to pick Susannah up from work? ....................................................

73  How do you know the Marathon race director was very pleased? ..........................................

74  What did the flight attendant refuse to do? ......................................................................................

75  What did Mr Gonzalez say? ......................................................................................

76  What did Grimes ask Harry about the dent in his car? ........................................................

77  'Melinda refused to see Damian again.' What do you think she actually said? ....................

78  What did the married couple do when they came out of church? ..........................................

79  How many forms has the word 'the' in your language? ........................................................

80  Why did Mrs Sharples want Gina to phone? ......................................................................................

## Unit 65

Key to crossword.

ACROSS  **1** wrist  **3** rash  **6** old  **7** prescribe  **9** heel  **10** vomit  **12** day  **13** spine  **14** graze  **15** ache  **16** eyes

DOWN  **1** whooping  **2** thermometer  **4** scarred  **5** rubella  **8** feverish  **11** tongue  **12** dizzy